The Red Rocks
of Eddystone

Books by the same author

THE MONASTERY

PATROL

CASSINO: PORTRAIT OF A BATTLE

FRED MAJDALANY

The Red Rocks
of Eddystone

LONGMANS

LONGMANS, GREEN AND CO LTD
6 & 7 CLIFFORD STREET, LONDON W I
THIBAULT HOUSE, THIBAULT SQUARE, CAPE TOWN
605-611 LONSDALE STREET, MELBOURNE C I
443 LOCKHART ROAD, HONG KONG
ACCRA, AUCKLAND, IBADAN
KINGSTON (JAMAICA), KUALA LUMPUR
LAHORE, NAIROBI, SALISBURY (RHODESIA)

LONGMANS, GREEN AND CO INC
119 WEST 40TH STREET, NEW YORK 18

LONGMANS, GREEN AND CO
20 CRANFIELD ROAD, TORONTO 16

ORIENT LONGMANS PRIVATE LTD
CALCUTTA, BOMBAY, MADRAS
DELHI, HYDERABAD, DACCA

© Fred Majdalany 1959

First Published 1959

Printed in Great Britain by Richard Clay and Company Ltd
Bungay, Suffolk

For
and in spite of
EMMA

Contents

Plates

Illustrations in the Text

ix

Acknowledgment

WE are indebted to Messrs. Thomas Nelson & Sons Ltd. for the use of copyright material from *English Lighthouse Tours*, ed. by D. Alan Stevenson.

Author's Note

I WISH to record my particular thanks to Captain Sir Gerald Curteis, K.C.V.O., R.N. (Retd.), Deputy Master of Trinity House, for his sympathetic interest and most generous assistance: not least for allowing me to be an exception to the rule that visitors are normally barred from rock lighthouses.

For valuable help with certain aspects of the research I am indebted to Mr. Edmund H. Watts: to Mr. W. Best Harris, City Librarian, and Mrs. Marion Beckford, of Plymouth Central Library: to Miss Gillian Chapman, M.A., Curator of Saffron Walden Museum: to Mr. F. G. Emmison, County Archivist to the County of Essex: to Mrs. Florence Winstanley Jerrard: and to the Hydrographer of the Navy.

Finally, for the fruits of his long experience in the lighthouse service, my thanks to Principal Keeper A. J. Freathy, my host during the time I spent on the Eddystone, where the first pages of this book were written.

F. M.

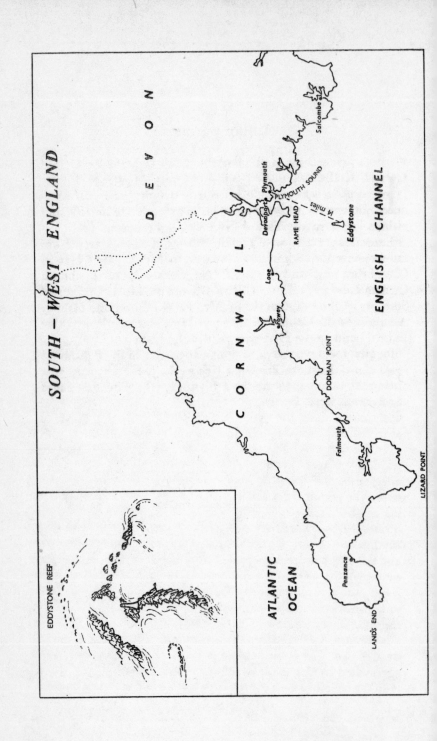

SOUTH – WEST ENGLAND

DEVON

CORNWALL

ENGLISH CHANNEL

ATLANTIC OCEAN

Salcombe

Plymouth
Devonport
PLYMOUTH SOUND
RAME HEAD
14 miles
Eddystone

Looe

Fowey

DODMAN POINT

Falmouth

Penzance

LAND'S END

LIZARD POINT

EDDYSTONE REEF

The Place

FOURTEEN miles to the south-west of Plymouth astride the approach to its great harbour, the fairway of the English Channel is broken by a triple reef. The rust-red rocks of which it is composed are a rare form of granitoid gneiss found in only one other area of the British Isles, at Prawle Point twenty-seven miles away: an indication that in the remote pre-Cambrian past the reef was joined to the mainland.

The most prominent of the three jagged ridges is the one in the centre which, except at high water, is exposed for two hundred yards and runs approximately from north to south. The other two splay outwards from it; the one to its west being fifty feet away, the other a hundred, but curving away to the east like a thumb. This red reef, which is called Eddystone, is part of an isolated underwater rock mass six hundred yards long, and rising steeply from the Channel bed. Because of its position and configuration the waters around it are nearly always rough even when the sea beyond is calm.

In the first place it is exposed to the full force of the westerly wind and current systems of the Atlantic. In the second, it is affected by the complex local tidal system. For the clash between the prevailing Atlantic drift from the west and the opposing northern current systems with which it collides beyond the Straits of Dover has given the English Channel a distinctive tidal rhythm of its own. Its tidal streams do not conform to the rise and fall of the lunar tides, but overlap them. Off Plymouth, for example, the stream normally ebbs three hours before high water, and floods during the last three hours to low water: but rough weather can upset these timings. This conflict between the rise and fall of the tide and the accompanying ebb and flow of the tidal stream gives the effect of four tides in twenty-four hours instead of two. The consequences of this at Eddystone are further aggravated by the shape of the rocks themselves.

In the course of time the Atlantic has worn down their western

sides to a gradual upward slope of about thirty degrees, so
that even in a moderate westerly sea the waves pile up to a great
height as they roll up this runway to break over the edge. On
the eastern side of each ridge the rocks drop vertically. As a
result an easterly swell, striking in rapid succession three broken
walls of rock, creates immense curtains of spray and an effect of
violence out of all proportion to its true power.

This is why it seems always to be rough at Eddystone; why
the reef appears to provoke a permanent chaos of currents and
eddies obeying no law; why the waters plunge and cascade into
the rocks from all directions at once. This is why in the first
place it was called Eddystone.

From the earliest times a legend of dread grew up around the
Eddystone, and as Plymouth grew in importance the legend
grew with it, for every year more and more ships were wrecked
on this reef. Its notoriety was reflected in a number of early
references.

The chronicler William of Worcester mentioned it in his
Itinerary of 1478. A century later Robert Newman described it
in a work which he called *A Safeguard For Sailors: or The Rutter of
the Sea*. In the first edition of his monumental *Britannia* published in 1586, Camden referred to the Eddystone as *scopulos
infamis—infamous rocks*, borrowing from Horace the phrase the
Roman poet applied to a similar hazard in the eastern Mediterranean. Hakluyt has a reference in his *Voyages* to ships being
wrecked on the Eddystone. For years it was nearly always referred to as the 'dreaded' Eddystone. Thus as late as 1839 we
find Robert Mudie writing in his *Companion to Gilbert's New Map
of England and Wales*: 'The once dreaded and dreadful rock of
the Eddystone, which literally means "the stone of the reeling
waves" a truly descriptive appellation, lies . . . near the point
where the strongest eddy of the bay holds conflict with the tide
round the Lizard.'

To the seamen of Devon who in the fifteenth and sixteenth
centuries were contributing so much to the future maritime
greatness of England, Eddystone at the end of the homeward
journey was a greater hazard than the open sea. To reach the
harbour-sanctuary of Plymouth they had to pass it. To avoid
it they would try to keep well to the south of it before making

their turn towards land. But this was a difficult course to judge, especially on a stormy night; and if they went too far to the south, as likely as not they would be driven on to the Casquets, a group of rocks off the Channel Islands. For the same west wind led that way too.

For years these sailors dreamed of the day when this reef might be marked in some way. This is the story of a few men of vision and courage who, over two centuries, dedicated themselves in turn to the supremely difficult and dangerous task of lighting the Eddystone rocks.

CHAPTER ONE

Ancient Lights

IT is difficult, in an age which has largely disarmed the ocean, to appreciate just what was involved in being a sailor even as recently as a century ago. In 1800 Lloyd's estimated the average loss of British ships to be about one a day. In 1830 the actual number of ships lost was 677. In a particularly black period of twenty-five years between 1854 and 1879—when the volume of shipping was of course much greater—the number of wrecks reached the appalling total of 49,322. In 1881 there were 973. Flying has never begun to exact a toll of human life comparable with that claimed, until modern times, by the sea. For the British this was the price of nationhood, and for those who sailed before ships were power-driven the most hazardous time of all was the approach to land.

Feeling his way with inadequate charts in what he hoped was the right direction, the mariner could only pray that the tentative blurred outline of the coast would soon clarify enough to reveal three or four familiar sea-marks: the oddly shaped rock, the unmistakable profile of a headland, the isolated clump of trees, the prominent white house. These were his signposts and his reference points as well as the first positive proof that the port ahead was the one he thought it was.

So sacred were these sea-marks that it was taken as a matter of course that they should not be removed or altered. An Act of Elizabeth I in 1566 made it a criminal offence to do so.

Forasmuch as by the destroying and taking away of certain steeples, woods and other marks standing upon the main shores adjoining to the sea coasts of this realm of England and Wales being as beacons and marks of ancient time accustomed for seafaring men . . . divers ships . . . have by the lack of such marks of late years been miscarried, perished and lost in the sea. . . .

Anyone removing such marks would in future be subject to a fine of £100, and if unable to pay the alternative was immediate outlawry.

Pepys, in his *Naval Minutes*, noted with disapproval that trees which had been an important sea-mark near Harwich were felled in 1673 to supply the King with carvings and that the Bishop of Winchester had been guilty of cutting down trees which for years had been familiar and important to ships approaching Portsmouth. It was always considered a matter of the highest urgency to restore or repair any spire or tower that was valuable as a sea-mark.

If it was an obvious policy of a maritime nation to preserve its established natural sea-marks with great care, and make it a criminal offence to change or remove them, it was equally natural to supplement them with artificial ones. From the earliest times the seafaring peoples did this. The beacon-tower is as old as the ship.

The Phoenicians, sailing from the Mediterranean as far north as Britain to trade textiles for Cornish tin, marked their route up western Europe with towers. The present lighthouse at Corunna is close to the site of one of them.

Those practical imperialists the Romans erected many such towers in their colonies, and from medallions we know what they looked like. The Pharos which they built at Dover—a fragment of it still survives—can claim to be the oldest lighthouse in England.

It is significant that two of antiquity's Seven Wonders of the World were sea-marks: the Colossus at Rhodes and the Pharos of Alexandria. The Colossus is better known through legend than fact. It was built about 300 B.C. by a pupil of Lysippus, the last and conceivably the greatest of the golden age of Greek sculptors. It was a bronze statue, probably of Apollo. It was about a hundred feet high, its feet rested on the two moles at the entrance of Rhodes harbour, and a ship in full sail could pass between its legs. It was destroyed by an earthquake in 224 after standing for about eighty years. The postscript to the story is that the bronze of the wrecked figure is supposed to have been sold by the Saracens to an Edessa Jew for the equivalent of £36,000. Legend does not, however, offer any

B

theory as to whether Arab or Jew was thought to have got the better of this particular deal.

More tenuous legend has added the suggestion that the god-figure held aloft a lighted torch, and that the Colossus was therefore a lighthouse as well as a sea-mark. In fact, no specific mention of this occurs in any of the ancient writers who refer to the work. There is no doubt at all, however, that the re-nowned Pharos at Alexandria was a lighthouse, sited on an island about a mile north of the port and linked to it by a causeway.

The building is generally attributed (on the authority of the Roman writer Strabo) to Sostratus in the reign of Ptolemy II, and one of the embellishments of the story has it that Sostratus recorded this fact in the outer wall of the building—but covered the lettering with mortar into which he cut a royal in-scription giving the credit to Ptolemy; the idea being that the mortar bearing Pharaoh's name would in time crumble away, exposing to the view of posterity the name of Sostratus.

Traditional estimates of the light's effective range have varied from a hundred miles to thirty-four. But these figures overlook the limits imposed by the earth's curvature on visibility at sea in accordance with the height of the light above it. To be visible at a distance of thirty-four statute miles the Pharos would have to have been 665 feet tall—and equipped with an exceptionally powerful light. In fact it now seems most probable that its height was about 350 feet—which is impressive enough.

The authority for this estimate is an eye-witness account of the Pharos written by a twelfth-century Arab historian, Ibn al-Shaikh. This important new evidence became known to Western scholars only in the present century. It inspired a new study of the Pharos by a Spanish scholar Don Miguel de Asin working in conjunction with an architect, Don M. Lopez Otero. Between them they have probably come closer than any previous author-ities to an accurate reconstruction of the Pharos.

According to their findings the tower was almost certainly in three sections. The lowest, a truncated pyramid, was ap-proximately 220 feet high; the middle section, a pyramidal octagon, just over 100 feet; the cylindrical upper portion just under 30 feet, this section being topped by the lantern. By any standards it must have been a remarkable building. In whole or in part it lasted some fifteen hundred years until the twelfth or thirteenth century when the remains finally crumbled away, assisted perhaps by the conquering and pillaging Ottoman armies.

By its very existence the Pharos pinpointed the supreme problem of the early navigator—the fear, not of the open sea, but of the rocks and shallows off the shore. In its grandeur it was antiquity's homage to the most hazardous and courageous of ancient callings.

The concept of the lighted sea-mark was a corollary to the idea of sailing the seas at all. It reached a premature apotheosis with the Pharos of Alexandria, and owed its subsequent practical development to the system of unspectacular, utilitarian beacon-towers left by the Romans among their legacies of empire. It was the French who were to provide the great historic link between the lighthouses of antiquity and those of modern times.

The Bay of Biscay owes its notoriety to more than the fact that its four-hundred-mile extent is wide open to the Atlantic. The agitation, for which its waters are notorious, is more particularly due to the dip of the sea-bed in the Gulf of Gascony—the elbow of Biscay roughly between the mouth of the Gironde and Biarritz. This sudden and extensive abyss has the effect of giving the bed of the bay the nature of a funnel. The Atlantic flood, plunging down this funnel and up again, creates vast opposing pressures and convulsions which turn the bay into a sort of Titan's whirlpool, and set in motion the Biscay swells which are one of the most devastating of the assault floods which bear down on the English Channel from the south-west.

Among the areas which catch the full impact of the bay at its worst is the estuary of the Gironde, as the confluence of the Garonne and Dordogne is named after the two rivers have joined near Bordeaux. Though the estuary is wide where it meets the sea, its entrance is cluttered up with a number of rocks and shoals, including the islet of Cordouan, a rock platform a thousand yards long and five hundred wide. At high water this long ledge is submerged.

In the ninth century, traders who came to Bordeaux to buy shipments of wine became so frightened of Cordouan that they threatened to stop coming until something was done to mark the island, and beacon-towers of sorts are known to have existed there since the year 880. They were scarcely adequate, however, and credit for putting up something better goes, a little surprisingly, to an Englishman.

Late in the sixteenth century—during that period of the Hundred Years War when Guienne was an English province and its governor the Black Prince had his court at Bordeaux—Edward, better known as a ruthless soldier, carried out at least one constructive act of administration: he arranged for a new lighthouse to be built on Cordouan. It was forty-eight feet high, and at the top of it there was a platform where a wood fire could be kept burning. To man this remote and inhospitable post, the Prince found an ideal person—a religious hermit. For this service, all ships passing the light were required to pay two groats (eightpence). And though it is not clear what proportion of this went to the hermit, and how much to his royal master, it is the first recorded instance of the payment of lighthouse dues, the system of financing the lighthouse service which has continued ever since.

In addition to the light tower, a small chapel was built on the islet, and a fishing community established itself there. It seems, however, that an adequate supply of successors to the hermit was not forthcoming. The tower fell into disrepair and disuse, and in the second half of the sixteenth century the Bordeaux wine men received another warning from their clients that they would be left with a surplus of unsold claret on their hands unless something was done to illuminate Cordouan properly. In 1584 work was started on a building destined to carry the lighthouse concept from one extreme to the other.

The creator of the new building was Louis de Foix, a leading Paris architect who had been one of the team of architects building the Escorial Palace for Philip II of Spain. The de Foix idea of a lighthouse was far removed from the simple beacon-towers to which he was to provide a successor. It must be nothing less than a Renaissance masterpiece. With a splendid disregard of expense, he planned an amalgam of royal palace, cathedral, and fort. At the top there would be a lantern, too, but this seemed almost incidental.

The islet of Cordouan, once linked with the mainland on the Medoc side of the estuary and still very accessible to it when the Black Prince's beacon was built, was now completely isolated. At high tide it was submerged, and numerous rocks made the approach to it difficult at all times. There was just one shingle beach in its thousand-yard length where a boat could be run ashore, and then only at low tide.

De Foix first built a round base, 135 feet in diameter and 8 feet high, which was solid except for a central cavity 20 feet square to be used as a cellar for the storage of water and other supplies. This massive platform was designed to take the main onslaught of the waves. It was a laborious task, and it took several years to complete. When it was finished de Foix really went to work. Four circular storeys of diminishing size were erected one above the other to form the tower. The ground floor consisted of a circular tower 50 feet in diameter, with apartments for four keepers around its inner wall. In the centre there was a richly decorated entrance hall 22 feet square and 20 high which appears to have had no other function than to impress visitors. The second storey was the King's Apartment, consisting of a drawing-room, ante-room, and a number of closets. The third storey was a chapel with a domed roof notable for the beauty of its mosaic. Above this was a secondary lantern room for occasional use when the main lantern was out of action. Finally, there was the lantern itself. Throughout the building, de Foix took as much trouble with the décor as with the durability of his building, and on every floor there was a profusion of gilt, carved work, elegantly arched doorways, and statuary.

Nothing if not prolific, de Foix took steps to ensure that the widest variety of classical styles should be provided for the distraction of sailors making use of his building to navigate the tricky waters over which it presided. Those mariners who were sufficiently well informed to know or care would notice that the pillars ornamenting the lowest storey of the lighthouse were Doric, those outside the next Ionic, the third Corinthian, and the fourth a mixture. Just how often the local clergy availed themselves of the opportunity to preach in the chapel is not recorded; nor is it clear whether any monarch, desirous of getting away from it all, ever made use of the beautiful royal suite provided on the first floor.

It comes as no surprise to learn that the Tour de Cordouan
took twenty-seven years to complete. It was started in 1584, in
the reign of Henry III, and finished in 1611, by which time
Louis XIII was king. The lantern was 162 feet above the sea
and visible five or six miles away, the original light being provided by the burning of oak chips in a metal container.

The French writer Belidor, who in 1743 published a description of the first Tour de Cordouan, thought it a pity that so
much architectural magnificence should have been expended
on so desolate and lonely a place. One can see his point.

But there are two observations to be made on this. First, the
prodigal spirit of the Renaissance was still strong. Secondly, in
all ages an aura of romance has attached itself to the concept of
the lighthouse. Louis de Foix was the first of the lighthouse
builders to challenge the open sea. It was a royal and romantic
assignment, and he had chosen to execute it in a royal manner.
The Tour de Cordouan has been called the Patriarch of Lighthouses, and the description is a fair one as it was indeed the
forerunner of the modern rock lighthouse.

The day would come when those concerned to make the seas a
little safer would look beyond the immediate coastline. Cordouan had shown what skill and dogged persistence could do
to erect a guiding beacon in an inaccessible and hostile place—
though the modern mind would agree with Belidor that something less ornate and elaborate, and taking less than twenty-
seven years to complete, might in the circumstances have been
more sensible. But its magnificence and the fame that went
with it were in the end a fine stimulus to others. Gradually the
coasts and the harbour entrances were being given marks of
identity. Cordouan had carried this a stage further to the erection, at a river mouth, of a durable lighthouse on an islet submerged for several hours of every day.

But what of the open sea, and that outer ring of rock outposts
beyond the immediate reach of land? Malignant reefs like the
Eddystone? Rocks barely large enough to contain the base of
a habitable building? After Cordouan the possibility that even
they would one day be tamed seemed a little less fantastic.

CHAPTER TWO

The Beginnings

PRACTICALLY nothing is known for certain about any English lighthouses between the Roman occupation and the middle of the seventeenth century except that a few primitive towers did exist, illumination being provided by coal or wood fires in braziers. The one at Lowestoft, known to be there in 1609, is generally credited with being the first, with those at Caister, Dungeness, and the Lizard running it close. But this cannot be stated as historical fact.

What is certain is that with the great expansion of maritime activity under the Tudors, there was a growing awareness of the need for a better system of sea-marks. The first positive action in this direction was taken by Elizabeth I. But the first constructive move towards a national policy—though not at first linked exclusively with the question of lighthouses—must be credited to Henry VIII.

Popular imagination, encouraged by the cinema, is inclined to dismiss Henry as a colourful Bluebeard with inelegant table manners. It overlooks the shrewd statesmanship for which he found time between marital crises. In particular, it is apt to forget that his imaginative reassessment of the importance of sea power to an island kingdom was one of the turning-points of English history.

It was Henry who first came to the conclusion that the way for an island nation to defend itself against an invader—especially an invader more powerful than itself—was to destroy him *at sea*. For this purpose, he decided, it was necessary to build ships designed purely for fighting—floating gun platforms. This thinking, which might now seem a little obvious, was at the time revolutionary. The navies of the day were not fighting forces but fleets of armed transports designed to carry soldiers. This was especially the case with Imperial Spain,

which then had the finest army in the world. In conceiving
and implementing the concept of the man-o'-war Henry in-
vented modern naval warfare, and his policy was to pay off
handsomely in the reign of his daughter Elizabeth when
Philip II, with the rest of Europe at his feet, dispatched his
Armada for a final showdown with England. For the essence of
that victory lay in the differing approaches to naval tactics of
the two sides. The Spanish tactical method—military rather
than naval—was to close with the enemy, board him, and fight
it out with soldiers: in other words, fight a land battle on board
ship. What wrecked their enterprise from the start was en-
countering the numerically smaller but better-gunned and
more manoeuvrable English fighting fleet, which prevented
the Spaniards from getting close enough to use their soldiers.

To ensure that his new policy worked, Henry next turned his
attention to the administrative side of the King's Navy Royal,
as it was then known, and established a Navy Board, which
was the forerunner of the present Board of Admiralty. This ensured that the Lord Admiral, the established head of the Navy
and an appointment acquired through social rather than technical qualifications, was backed by a committee of practical
administrators to deal with the more humdrum day-to-day
running of the service, which might prove beyond the inclina-
tion or the capacity of His Lordship.

Having attended to policy and administration, Henry completed his reforms by creating a body of experts in maritime
matters who, acting in a supervisory capacity, would ensure the
maintenance of proper standards in all matters pertaining to
ships and seamanship: a sort of Royal Academy of the Sea. So
there came into being one of the most colourful and esoteric of
those bodies corporate which are so much a part of the English
tradition.

Today the Corporation of Trinity House is one of the most
venerable national institutions. Under the financial control
of the Ministry of Transport and Civil Aviation it is responsible
for the management of the lighthouses, lightships, and buoyage
of England and Wales. It is the principal pilotage authority for
the United Kingdom and, in addition, it administers a number

of charities connected with the sea and the welfare of seamen.

Trinity House is run by a Deputy Master and a body of
Elder Brethren, all of whom are former ships' captains of dis-
tinction. It is presided over by an Honorary Master, who for
nearly a century has been a member of the Royal Family, and
a dozen Honorary Elder Brethren who represent a cross-
section of the most illustrious Englishmen of the day. Such is
the aura attaching to the Corporation that to be elected one of
its Honorary Elder Brethren has become one of the culminating
distinctions coveted by eminent men already sated with
honours.

Former Prime Ministers who have been elected to this exclusive club have included Gladstone, Baldwin, Churchill,
Eden, and Attlee. The roll of Elder Brethren in 1959 included
(in addition to Sir Winston and Earl Attlee) Prince Philip, The
Duke of Windsor, Admiral Earl Mountbatten, and Field-
Marshal Viscount Alexander. Since 1942 His Royal Highness
the Duke of Gloucester has been Master.

Although they take no active part in the Corporation's business, Honorary Elder Brethren love being Elder Brethren, an
appointment which carries with it the right to wear an elegant
quasi-Naval uniform. Sir Winston Churchill has always delighted in this uniform. He wore it for his first historic meeting
at sea with President Roosevelt during the Second World War:
and again after the War at a victory celebration in France, when
it greatly intrigued his French hosts. Asked what it was, he replied with pride: '*Je suis frère aîné de la Trinité.*' Which prompted
a Frenchman present to murmur: '*Mon Dieu! Quelle influence!*'
The French have always been a little confused by the Corporation's name. When Gladstone was elected an Elder Brother a
Paris newspaper informed its readers that he had retired from
politics to enter a religious house, La Maison de la Trinité.

Even the average Englishman, suddenly confronted by a
question about the function of Trinity House, would probably be
unable to go further than to say that he thought it had something to do with lighthouses. For like all ancient foundations
that have evolved through the centuries in a tradition of con-
servatism and exclusiveness, the Corporation shrinks from

publicity. As it happens, it has been assisted in this desire for privacy by the unhappy chance that on no fewer than three occasions its records have been destroyed by fire. The first time was in the Great Fire of London in 1666; the second in 1714; the third during the blitz in 1940.

As a result of this habitual annihilation of its records, Trinity House can with certainty trace its existence only as far back as the year 1512, though it believes that its ancestry goes back farther.

In 1512 Henry VIII granted to a group of master mariners a licence to form a guild 'in honour of the Holy Trinity and Saint Clement in the Church of Deptford Strond for the re-formation of the navy, lately much decayed by admission of young men without experience and of Scots, Flemings and Frenchmen as lodesmen'—lodesman being the contemporary term for pilot.

In 1514 the Guild was formally incorporated by the King as 'The Brotherhood of the Most Glorious and Undividable Trinity', and the 'Brethren and Sisters of the same' were granted 'power and authority' to take any steps they thought desirable 'for the relief, increase and augmentation of the ship-ping of this our Realm of England'. The Guild had the power to make any laws they considered necessary to carry out their duty and to try to punish anyone who broke them.

Deptford, now an indistinguishable part of the Port of London mass, was at the time the base of the Thames pilots. St. Clement, whose martyrdom took the form of being thrown into the sea tied to an anchor, was held by some to be the patron saint of sailors. Scots, Flemings, and Frenchmen were what would now be called bad security risks, and it was con-sidered foolish that intimate knowledge of home waters should be almost exclusively in their hands. Just what the Sisters were supposed to contribute to 'the augmentation of shipping' is not clear. The Brethren must also have had their doubts, as, in accordance with English club tradition, they were never heard of again after the original charter.

Such was the origin of the Corporation of Trinity House, the simpler name which the fraternity subsequently adopted. Al-though there was not in the first place any specific mention of sea-marks, it might have been expected that the Corporation would turn their minds to that subject, since it was an obvious aspect of the general welfare of shipping for which they had been made responsible. It was in fact fifty-one years before the matter came up officially.

The Charter of Henry VIII was confirmed by Edward VI in 1547, Mary in 1553, and Elizabeth I in 1558. It was in 1566, the eighth year of Elizabeth's reign, that an Act of Parliament formally conferred on the Master, Wardens, and Assistants of Trinity House two new powers. One was the control and licensing of Thames pilots. The other authorized the Brethren

> from time to time . . . and at their costs to make, erect, and set as such and so many beacons, marks, and signs for the sea, in such place or places of the sea-shores, and uplands near the sea-coasts . . . as to them shall seem most meet needful and requisite, whereby the dangers may be avoided and escaped, and ships the better come into their ports without peril. And that all such beacons marks and signs . . . set up at the costs and charges of the said Master, Wardens and Assistants, shall and may be continued, renewed and maintained from time to time, at the costs and charges of the said Master, Wardens and Assistants. . . .

This was the Act, referred to earlier, which also made it a criminal offence to remove any natural sea-mark.

The Act of 1566 was followed up in 1593 by a Grant of the Queen, which made it clear that the authority to set up beacons, marks, and buoys was conferred *exclusively* on Trinity House. These two dates mark the beginning of a national lighthouse policy in any recognizable form. The first Act had recognized that the lighthouse was as integral a part of a national maritime policy as ships. The later Grant attempted to give practical effect to this principle by placing the matter in the charge of a central authority.

But though Trinity House took its monopoly rights seriously, practically no one else did, and it was to be a long time— nearly two and a half centuries—before the lighthouses of England and Wales were all in the hands of the Corporation. It was a century, too, before these new arrangements produced a lighthouse of any note. And then it was not Trinity House who built it!

From the first there were interests which regarded with jealousy and resentment the growing power of the Corporation. It was contemporaneous with, and growing alongside, the new Navy born of the reforms of Henry VIII, and there were many points at which the two bodies overlapped. Trinity House had control of certain naval installations—the dockyard at Deptford, for instance. It ran charitable trusts connected with the Navy; it advised the judges in court cases concerned with shipping matters; it examined naval officers; its powers were constantly increasing.

The Act of 1566 had given it control of pilots and the right to build beacons and sea-marks. In this Act Elizabeth had referred to the brethren as 'A Corporation of the chiefest and most expert of masters and governors of ships incorporate within themselves, charged with the conduction of the Queen Majesty's Navy Royal'. Just how far was 'conduction' expected to go? The Grant of 1593 (besides conferring the monopoly control of lighthouses) had passed to Trinity House certain other rights formerly belonging to the Lord Admiral. The relationship between Trinity House and the Navy seems at this time to have borne a strong resemblance to that of the chicken and the egg, with an ever-present doubt as to which came first. There was much scope for friction between the two, and evidence, despite the loss of so many records, that it periodically took a heated form. Some acid exchanges of correspondence survive.

Whereas the Navy's attitude was understandably a matter of Service pride, in the case of another group hostile to the growing influence of Trinity House it was simpler. It was a matter of the pocket.

In the forefront of those who resented the idea of the Brethren taking over the lighting of the coasts were the men who happened to own such lighthouses as then existed. Not for the last time in English history private enterprise found its existence threatened by a central monopoly and prepared to fight it to the death. It was destined to be a long battle, for private enterprise had a valuable ally, the Crown itself.

The system was simple. Men of substance purchased from the Sovereign a licence to erect a beacon. They then collected dues from all ships passing by. From the income thus provided the Sovereign was given a rake-off. Since Sovereigns were invariably short of cash, this allotting of lighthouses had grown into a highly valuable sideline. The only losers were the unfortunate sailors intended to benefit from the lighthouses, for the majority of these lighthouse-owners were concerned with profit rather than service, and many of their so-called beacons were little more than token affairs of little use to anyone.

How Queen Elizabeth—always willing to accept her cut of the Spanish plunder brought back by Drake and Company from their skirmishes with the Spaniards—overlooked this convenient source of income is a mystery. It is possible that, being a woman as well as a queen, she simply considered that the monopoly rights she had conferred on Trinity House did not affect her own position. Perhaps, in return for the monopoly, Trinity House did a deal with her which has not found its way into the records. At all events her canny Scottish successor James I had other views.

Like his predecessors, James renewed the Trinity House Charter. He even went so far as to make an Order in Council confirming the lighthouse monopoly. Having done this (perhaps he signed it without reading it), he ordered the Attorney-General, Sir Francis Bacon, to look into the matter more closely with a view to finding a legal loophole. Of course there was none. The Grant of Elizabeth, confirmed by himself, was perfectly explicit: lighthouses were the exclusive province of Trinity House. Bacon, faced with a prickly dilemma that could cost him his head, ingeniously fell back on a shifty adaptation of the render-unto-Caesar principle. He decided that there was no doubt that all rights in all matters pertaining to lighthouses did legally belong to Trinity House. But he saw no reason in law why the King should not also issue licences and patents: the Throne was back in the lighthouse business.

Applications began to come in. Sir William Erskine obtained a patent to build a lighthouse at Winterton in Lincolnshire. Peter Frobisher, son of Sir Martin Frobisher, was granted a patent to build one at Ravenspur, despite the fact that Trinity House strongly opposed the project. The King was to receive £6 13s. 4d. annually for this particular property. Some years later the diary of Lord Grenville contained this revealing note. '*Mem:* To watch the moment when the King is in a good temper, to ask of him a lighthouse.'

Battle was now joined in earnest, and in 1621 the Brethren won a round. They managed to get a Bill through Parliament ordering the suppression of the private lighthouses in Norfolk on the grounds of neglect. But a year or two later they were less successful.

Sir John Killigrew, one of the more thrustful lighthouse speculators, who had already set up a light at the Lizard, wished to erect two new lighthouses which he claimed would be helpful to ships wishing to avoid the Goodwin Sands. Trinity House opposed the project on three reasonable grounds. They claimed that these lighthouses would be of no use whatever; that the proposed levy of twopence a ton would be a great hardship to shipowners; and that all pilots familiar with the area stated that there had been no losses of ships there within memory. In spite of this, Killigrew got his way.

In view of the part played by the Throne in thwarting Trinity House in its concern for standards generally and the sailor's welfare in particular, it is ironical that the Brethren's next rebuff should have come from Cromwell—on the grounds that the Corporation was too Royalist! In 1647 the Trinity House Charter was dissolved and a committee of Roundheads took over, but after the Restoration in 1660 Charles II put things right and the Brethren were free to resume their uphill battle with the private owners.

Shortly after this, Trinity House was reinforced by the colourful and purposeful presence of Samuel Pepys as an Elder Brother and, for two separate terms of a year, as Master. His diary has some irreverent comments on the Brethren. On one occasion he refers to them as 'the old sokers'. On another he writes: 'I found them reading their Charter which they did like fools, only reading here and there a bit, whereas they ought to do it all, every word . . .' One Elder Brother is described as a 'lazy, corrupt, doating Rogue', and in the *Naval Minutes* covering the 1680–83 period he is moved to remark: 'Even the Trinity House grown corrupt and useless!'

But this is an incidental side of the picture. Pepys the amusing gossip was one thing. Pepys, Secretary to the Admiralty, and Elder Brother of Trinity House, was an able administrator who threw his weight into the Corporation's struggle with the private owners. He also had a big hand in a scheme which, though not strictly relevant to this story, is worth mentioning in passing, as it throws a light on the sort of way in which it was possible to make use of the expertise and authority of Trinity House in matters generally concerned with the welfare of shipping.

This was the establishment by Charles II at Christ's Hospital School of a Mathematical Wing designed to give specialized instruction in mathematics and other subjects concerned with navigation. The purpose was to create a supply of potential ships' masters. These forty boys were in effect a class of King's Scholars, living a privileged group life within the framework of the school, but supervised and examined by Trinity House. The fact that this duty was allotted to Trinity House rather than to the Navy is an indication that despite its detractors, the Corporation was well established as the supreme academic authority in matters to do with the sea.

Whatever he may privately have recorded about some of his colleagues, Pepys went all the way with them in their efforts to solve the lighthouse problem. He periodically made tours of inspection and spoke frankly of what he found. He denounced the system of private ownership more than once. On one occasion he noted that a certain owner had five lights and that none of them was of any use. He denounced another for having a light where, so far from being a help, it was actually a danger to shipping. But it was of little avail. The stalemate went on, and as the century slipped by it seemed that the Elizabethan moves towards a national lighthouse service had become a few scraps of paper in the State Archives; and that Trinity House, which should have been lending its knowledge and energies to making the policy come true, was increasingly engaged, not in building lighthouses itself, but in trying to prevent others from doing so.

While the struggle between the private owners and the Brethren dragged itself on at Court, in Parliament, and in the law courts, there was a less-exalted category of men who watched the situation with close interest—those members of the population who lived on the proceeds of shipwreck.

It is a regrettable fact that for every man willing to risk his life at sea there were dozens hoping not only that he would be shipwrecked near their particular piece of coast, but were willng to help bring this about. Wrecking is an ancient business that has been practised in every country with a sea-board. The Greeks and Romans used to take charge of the cargo and sell any survivors as slaves. The fifteenth- and sixteenth-century inhabitants of the British Isles preferred to kill the survivors, as there was a superstition that they would bring bad luck if they lived.

The stories of the wreckers and their ways belong more to the folklore of the sea than to its history, but it is beyond doubt that, whatever colourful embroidery they may have acquired in the retelling, in their essentials they are grimly founded on fact. It goes without saying that these people were not content to rely on the elements for their supply of loot, but took active steps to encourage shipwreck. It was a simple matter to set a light where it would lure a ship on to the rocks, or to hang a lantern on a horse's tail so that on a dark night it could be mistaken for the swinging light of another ship. It was equally simple to change the position of guiding lights already known to the potential victim. There was a rich harvest to be reaped during these years in which trade was expanding almost weekly. It was not surprising that the Scilly Islanders were able to make their fences of the finest mahogany, or that crofters in the Western Highlands of Scotland were developing a taste for brandy or claret in their porridge.

A stranger visiting the Farne Islands off the north-east coast of England was charmed by the natives' habit of going down on their knees in prayer whenever a ship was sighted during stormy weather, until he discovered that they were praying that it would be wrecked on their own particular beach.

After the profitable wreck of a ship named *Eliza* on the Devon coast, the beneficiaries were even provided by a local poet with a song of triumph which began:

The *Eliza* of Liverpool came to shore
To feed the hungry and clothe the poor.

When Sir John Killigrew obtained his patent to build a light-house on the Lizard Point, Trinity House was not the only opposition he encountered. The inhabitants of the remote head-land were as hostile to the project as the Brethren, though for different reasons. This was one of the best wrecking areas in Cornwall. Almost every house on it was built of the timbers of wrecked ships and furnished with their contents. Only re-cently they had enjoyed a notable windfall in the form of £3,000 of silver taken from a Dutch ship which had foundered near the Point. Now some fool wanted to spoil the pitch with a lighthouse! So they petitioned (unsuccessfully) against the erection of Killigrew's light on the ground that it would 'take away God's grace' from them and they would have no more 'benefits from shipwrecks'.

In Brittany, as in Cornwall, wrecking was a major industry, and the story is told of a Compte St. Leon who was being urged by a jeweller to buy some precious stones. The Compte led him to a window, and pointing to a prominent rock that had caused more than one wreck, said that it was a much more valuable stone than anything the jeweller could offer.

On the Wolf Rock, between Land's End and the Scillies, there was a great cave which used to create a curious sound effect. When heavy seas and high winds drove into it from the south-west the cave emitted a wolf-like howl. It was from this that the rock got its name, and as it was audible a long way off, it was a valuable warning signal to ships in the vicinity. Indeed, it was so successful that Cornish wreckers decided to silence it— which they did by filling the cave up with stones which they transported from Land's End, nine miles away. After this there were enough wrecks to keep even the Cornishmen happy.

It was a hard world in which to be a sailor.

Towards the end of the seventeenth century, a hundred years of wrangling between Trinity House and the private owners had produced the unimpressive total of fifteen lighthouses around the coasts of England and Wales. (Ireland had six, Scotland one.) The majority were still privately owned, and most of them were inefficient.

One's sympathies lean towards the Brethren. Their attitude,

c

if sometimes autocratic and unyielding, was at least disinterested. They were not in business for profit: any income
from their various activities was supposed to be devoted to their
charities. Their standards, though conservative and often
over-cautious, were those of a professional guild conscious of its
trust. The alliance of Big Business and the Crown which they
had to face was a difficult one to beat. At the same time this
hardly justifies the fact that the Corporation's attitude so often
seemed to be negative. The energy which was so assiduously
devoted to opposing the plans of others might more usefully
have been employed in setting an example by erecting better
lighthouses of their own.

It is significant that when in the last years of the century a
project came into being which in boldness of conception and
imaginative daring was to eclipse anything that had gone before, it was not Trinity House who conceived it but, once again,
private enterprise. But private enterprise of a calibre very
different from the blatant profiteers on whom the sailor had
previously been mainly dependent for the few miserable coastal
lights provided for his safety.

CHAPTER THREE

Plymouth Insists

THE seventeenth century was kind to Plymouth. By the end of it the city had doubled in size. Trade was expanding all the time, and Plymouth was enjoying its full share. The buccaneering tradition of the Sea Dogs in the previous century was a distant memory. The emphasis now was on a steadily growing mercantile marine. The great harbour at the western end of England was still a main home of the Navy, but increasing numbers of merchant vessels now crowded its expansive waters. Plymouth, which had sent many men to the New World, was doing more and more business with their grandchildren. The three-year siege during the Civil War had, of course, been a hard interlude. But Plymouth, always tough, had emerged from it tougher and all the more self-confident. It would never have crossed the minds of these proud tough Nonconformist men of Devon that their harbour wasn't the finest in the world, their seamen the very best.

Only one thing marred their pride in what they had to offer. The Eddystone rocks. Year after year the Eddystone was claiming its victims, and because so many more ships were now sailing to and from Plymouth, the number of victims was rising. The ships were getting bigger, too, and the cargoes more valuable, so that their loss seemed all the more shocking. Eddystone was the one blot on an otherwise fair prospect. Whenever Plymouth was feeling pleased with itself there was always at the back of its mind, to spoil the effect, the haunting thought of the Eddystone reef. It made a mockery of the superb harbour, it was a slur on civic pride, it was a personal affront, and for years there was talk that something should be done about it. But what?

Quite early in the century Admiral Sir William Monson, in a letter discussing the necessity for a light on the Lizard Point not many miles up the coast, had added that it was even more important that the Eddystone should be marked in some way. But no one had cared to take him up on this. Then in 1664 the first practical move was made. Two leading Plymouth citizens, Sir John Coryton and a Mr. H. Brunker, petitioned Trinity House for leave to erect a lighthouse on the reef. They enlisted the support of the Duke of York, who personally presented the petition. The Brethren, one is hardly surprised to learn, rejected it out of hand. There the matter rested for thirty years. The westerly gales and the great driving swells from Biscay continued to feed the Eddystone rocks with a regular sacrificial ration of wrecks. On many occasions the owners of these ships, peering tensely through their telescopes from Plymouth Hoe, had no alternative but to watch their final death agonies—though more often the end came at night and all that would be known was that some ship that had been sighted off another part of the coast some hours before no longer existed.

In 1688 Plymouth once again found itself at the centre of a national upheaval, the so-called Glorious Revolution which deposed James II and brought William of Orange to the English throne in his place. Plymouth had been quick to support the Roundheads in the Civil War: in the new crisis it was the first city in England to declare its allegiance to Protestant William when he landed at Torbay. William brought his fleet of four hundred ships round to Plymouth, where he received a hero's welcome, and there the fleet remained through the winter while the final settlement of the Revolution was being effected in Ireland and London. William also took an immediate fancy to Hamoaze, the larger of the two inner waterways of Plymouth harbour, and decided to establish there his main naval arsenal. This was the beginning of what was later to become Devonport Dockyard, and it gave a new importance to Plymouth as a naval base. With a new dynasty; a new king who seemed both amenable and constructive; a new importance for Plymouth through the expansion of its naval base—the time was propitious for bringing up once again the question of the Eddystone.

There was now a militant public opinion to back the new campaign. All the time skilled and gallant sailors were losing their lives, shipowners were losing their ships, merchants were losing valuable cargoes from America and the Far East. This was an issue which affected many sections of the population, and the West Country was becoming angry, as were the increasing numbers of London merchants who depended on the port of Plymouth. Trinity House could no longer resist the pressure. It brought the matter to the notice of the Throne, and the result was a Patent Roll signed by William and Mary on 22 June, 1694, the essence of which is contained in the following extract:

> Whereas the Master Wardens and Assistants of the Trinity House . . . have represented unto us that Application has been made to them by the masters and owners of Shipping trading to all parts Westward of Plymouth . . . to erect a Light house or Beacon with a light upon the Rock called the Eddystone off Plymouth . . . as safe directions for ships hereafter to avoid that dangerous Rock upon which the lives of so many of our good Subjects have perished, and that in consideration of the vast charge and hazard of such an Undertaking the said masters and owners do voluntarily offer and agree to pay to the said Master Wardens and Assistants . . . one penny per tunn outward and the like inward for all ships and vessels passing by the said lighthouse (excepting Coasters who are to pay but twelve pence p. voyage). . . . Now know yee that Wee . . . doe give and grant . . . the Master Wardens and Assistants of the Trinity House . . . Authority that they may demand collect and take of the Merchants and Owners of Shipps, Hoys and Barks which shall passe by the said Light house intended to bee erected on the said Eddystone . . . the Duty of One penny per tunn outward bound and alsoe one penny per tunn inward excepting Coasters from whom we doe . . . give Authority . . . to take twelve pence for each Voyage passing by the said lighthouse or beacon and noe more.

The Patent further laid down that the port authorities were to ensure that no ship was unloaded or serviced until these lighthouse dues had been paid. Dues would be payable from the time the new structure first showed a light.

It was a wonderful opportunity for Trinity House to assert the pre-eminence in the lighthouse field it had for so long claimed. This was the most spectacular and ambitious lighthouse project there had ever been. Trinity House had been given full authority to go ahead with it in the knowledge that they would receive the fullest co-operation in collecting the highly profitable dues that would be theirs once it was in operation. It might be thought that the Corporation would have seized the chance eagerly. This was not, however, the case. For two years they did nothing. Then, in 1696, the Brethren—who for more than a century had been denouncing the iniquity of allowing lighthouses to be privately owned—handed over the Eddystone project to private enterprise! They concluded a deal with a Plymouth man named Walter Whitfeld; but at terms highly advantageous to themselves. It is not too difficult to guess the reasons for this curious change of attitude.

First, there was the sheer difficulty of the job itself. Any fool could stick up a tower of sorts on land. It was a somewhat different proposition to set a durable structure on a small wave-swept cluster of rocks ten miles from the nearest point of land, fourteen miles from Plymouth, and exposed to the full force of the Atlantic. It was a daunting idea, and the Brethren were clearly daunted by the thought of it.

Secondly, there was the matter of finance. The legislation of Queen Elizabeth which the Brethren were always dragging up in support of their claim to be solely responsible for lighthouses had, it is true, given them an exclusive right to build them. Unhappily it had added the words 'at their costs'. It is a characteristic of official bodies that, while aggressively eager to assert and defend their rights, when the question of risking their own money arises, their pride is often tempered all of a sudden by caution. The Eddystone enterprise was extremely risky, and it was going to be exceedingly costly. It is evident that the Brethren did not fancy the idea at all. Perhaps there was, after all, something to be said for those rascally private owners. There was one way to silence the nagging of these impatient, persistent West Countrymen. Let them get on with the job themselves.

The terms of the deal which Trinity House worked out with Whitfeld are illuminating. He and his associates were to build the lighthouse and to stand the entire financial risk. To help them recover this capital outlay, they were to receive the whole of the dues that came in during the first five years of the lighthouse's existence. For the next fifty years the income would be shared with Trinity House on a fifty-fifty basis. After that Trinity House would take the lot. From the point of view of the Brethren it was a good arrangement. Without risking a penny they stood to gain a considerable income if the venture succeeded. If it failed they lost nothing. It may be thought that on this occasion the Brotherhood of the most Glorious and Undividable Trinity and of St. Clement was a little closer to Mammon than to God.

The question now was to find a man capable of tackling the job and willing to do so. Where among the architects of England was the Theseus who would slay the monster of Eddystone? There was the great Sir Christopher Wren, then at the height of his powers. But he was hardly likely to be attracted by such an assignment. In any case he was still occupied with the re-building of St. Paul's, destroyed in the Great Fire. Two years before, in 1694, the new cathedral had been opened for the first time for public worship, but it would be another sixteen years before the great dome was finished, and throughout this time he and his assistants were also hard at work on the fifty-four City of London churches that Wren had designed. There could be no help from them—nor, as it turned out, from any other architectural quarter. And civil engineers, in any modern sense, just did not exist.

There was, as it happened, a man willing to take on the in-timidating task. A remarkable man, a man of many parts: engraver, showman, conjuror, illusionist, designer, inventor, practical joker, publicist, painter, pamphleteer, eccentric, and business-man. He was all these things, but by no stretch of imagination could he be described as an architect or an en-gineer, the two qualifications one would have thought indis-pensable in the circumstances. His name was Henry Win-stanley.

CHAPTER FOUR

'My Lord's Porter'

ENRY WINSTANLEY was born in 1644 at Saffron Walden in Essex, then as now one of those sleepy English market towns which history considerately contrives to leave largely untouched. His father was the bailiff and accountant of the Earl of Suffolk's palace at Audley End a mile away. He was responsible for the estate accounts, the collecting of rents, and the payment of wages and other household expenses. He was able to find work for his son there, and at the age of twenty-one young Winstanley was working as a junior assistant in the estate offices. An entry in the household accounts of 1665 notes the payment of five shillings to 'Mr. Henry Winstanley, my lord's porter'. But it was not long before Henry began to display talents which indicated that he would not remain an office boy for long. He could draw and he had a natural gift for inventing mechanical gadgets, an early effort in the latter direction being the equipping of the parish church with an elaborate clock, on the face of which representations of the sun and the moon circulated in orbit. The local people were delighted with this elementary demonstration of basic astronomy and paid him £108 for the clock which soon went wrong and, after many attempts to repair it, had eventually to be scrapped. But this was just a beginning.

Audley End had been built by the first Earl of Suffolk sixty years before, and its original form was considered to outshine in magnificence even the royal palace of Hampton Court. At the time Suffolk was Lord High Treasurer of England. Among his earliest guests was James I. After showing him over the place Suffolk asked him what he thought of it. With a bleak smile the King said it was 'good enough for a Lord High Treasurer, but too good for a king.'

It is not always wise for a courtier to have a better home than

his sovereign, and the third Earl possibly had this in mind when
he sold the palace to Charles II. Charles made good use of
Audley End (which he renamed the New Palace) and frequently transferred his Court there. For a frivolous monarch,
whose pleasure was evenly divided between bed and horse-
racing, the palace was ideally situated on the London–Newmarket road forty miles from the capital, twenty from Newmarket. In addition, Nell Gwyn had taken a fancy to a house
in the pretty village of Newport only five miles along the road,
and it was most convenient to have her lodging there while the
Court was at Audley End. Among the appurtenances that went
with Audley End were the services of this lively young man,
Henry Winstanley, of whom people spoke so highly and
generally with amusement.

The self-portrait which Winstanley left behind—it hangs in
the Saffron Walden Museum—is revealing. It is a handsome,
arresting face with a full sensual mouth, broad flat nose and
slanting astigmatic eyes that are both cruel and humorous: an
actor's face with a hint of an inward sardonic smile: the smile,
perhaps, of a perverted male Mona Lisa.

Henry Winstanley had little difficulty in ingratiating himself
with the new royal master of Audley End. Though still very
young, he had by this time travelled extensively in France,
Germany, and Italy and had returned from these journeys with
his already vivid imagination greatly stimulated. Winstanley,
man of ideas, was ready to put his volatile brain to full use, and
the link with the royal entourage at Audley End was going to
be most helpful.

He married a local girl, a Miss Taylor, and built a house in
Littlebury, a village two miles from Audley End along the road
which the King had to take on his visits to Mistress Gwyn
three miles farther on. It was, to say the least, an unusual
home, and the former Miss Taylor must have been an accommodating wife.

A low fence surrounded the house and a turnstile took the
place of a gate. The front of the house was adorned with a
clock on one side, a weather-glass on the other. The roof was
crowned with a large lantern on which stood a weather-vane.
In the back garden there was a windmill which pumped water,

a facility in advance of its time. This was just the beginning. It
was inside the house that the bizarre humour of Henry Winstanley really let itself go.

It was filled with fun-fair devices for disconcerting the visitor:
objects lying about the floor which caused an apparition to appear when they were kicked aside, illusory effects with mirrors,
trick chairs of various kinds. One of these snapped its arms
across anyone who sat on it, pinioning him until Winstanley
came to the rescue. It seems a pity that the Winstanleys never
had children.

But however much Winstanley may have enjoyed watching
the discomfiture of his victims, it is clear that the house was
primarily designed to make money. There was the turnstile to
register the number of visitors, and the contents of the house
were widely advertised as Winstanley's Wonders. As their fame
spread increasing numbers of people came to see them, some of
them travelling great distances to do so, like the Ustickes who
lived near Land's End. William Usticke made a tour of
England on horseback, his wife riding pillion, his cousin Tresillian riding with them for company. Land's End is a long way
from Littlebury, but these travellers knew all about Winstanley's Wonders, and their visit to the house was one of the
highlights of their tour. This was how William Usticke described it in his diary:

> We visited ye famous Mr. Winstanley's ingenious contrivances,
> viz., at ye taking up a slipper appeared ye form of a ghost which
> arose from ye planching and disappeared again. A small pair of
> organs played a tune at your winding up. One chair as my
> Cousin Tresillian sat in it descended perpendicularly about ten
> feet in a dark and dismal place. Another chair as he sat in it ran
> ye length of a small orchard and over a moat, jumped up in a tree,
> then descended and in a very little time stopped. A seat in ye
> garden was changed into several shapes. . . . We gave each a
> shilling to see ye house.

Cousin Tresillian, at least, seems to have had full value for
his shilling.

It is likely that several of these trick effects were the product
of Winstanley's travels in Italy. Horace Walpole thought so.

Clearly not an enthusiastic client of the Littlebury fun-fair,
Walpole has a sour note on the subject:

> These childish contrivances I suppose he learned in Italy where
> they do not let their religion monopolise all kinds of legerdemain.
> In the Villa Borghese at Rome amidst emperors, heroes and
> philosophers, I have seen a puppet-show in a box that turned like
> a squirrel's rolling cage. In the same palace was a noble statue of
> Seneca lying in the bath and a Devil that started out of a clock-
> case as you entered the chamber.

If the level of fun seems simple, it should be remembered that
this was the period of the Restoration. England was revelling
in a boisterous reaction against the austerities of the Puritans.
With the Merry Monarch setting the pace, fun was unin-
hibited and hearty. With its huge lantern shining out a welcome over the main road the extraordinary house of Winstanley's Wonders would be a natural stopping-place for the
undergraduates who passed this way to and from Cambridge;
for the young bloods of the horsey set returning from Newmarket in their cups; for members of the Royal Household at
Audley End; and for Charles himself driving past on his way
to or from the embraces of Nell Gwyn a mile or two up the road.
There is no specific record that Mrs. Winstanley augmented the
box-office takings and the enjoyment of the customers by serving
refreshments, but it would be in keeping with neither the spirit
of the age nor the business acumen of the Winstanleys if she
did not.

The freak house at Littlebury was only one of Winstanley's
concerns at this time. He was also making use of his ability as a
draughtsman. He was working on a set of drawings and sketches
covering the whole of Audley End Palace, and he had hit on the
idea of inviting the noblemen of England to commission him
to make engravings of their stately homes at five pounds a time.
He also produced a number of novelties, including a pack of
playing-cards.

These cards, in addition to being elaborately decorative, in-
corporated some mild geographical instruction on the side.
Each suit was represented by a continent: Spades by Africa,
Hearts by Europe, Diamonds by Asia, and Clubs by America.

Two of Winstanley's Playing Cards.

Not content with this, Winstanley, who never did things by halves, added further identifications to the four suits, Europe (Hearts) being distinguished by roses, Asia (Diamonds) by the sun, Africa (Spades) by the moon, and America (Clubs) by a star. There was no excuse for revoking when playing with a pack of these cards. Each of the fifty-two cards carried an illustrated note on a town or country of the continent represented by its suit. The Eight of Clubs, for instance, is headed Santa Fé and begins:

> California most Properly is a great Island in the Mare Pacifique or South Sea little discovered or inhabited but with Savages . . .

Many packs of Winstanley's Geographical Playing Cards were distributed, and at least one found its way to America. It was picked up in New Jersey late in the nineteenth century by a New York collector. The British Museum has an incomplete set of forty-one cards bound in the form of a small book.

It is scarcely surprising that Charles II, not the most serious of kings, was delighted to find such a man on his pay-roll at Audley End and in due course made him his Clerk of the Works both for Audley End and his property at Newmarket. An insight into his character is provided by his invariable habit of signing his work 'Henry Winstanley, Gent. . . .' His insistence on that 'Gent.' arouses the suspicion that his immediate male forebears may not have been strictly entitled to the rank. The royal appointment must have been doubly pleasing to him. Prosperous, famous, and now socially established in the most flattering way possible, Winstanley embarked on his most ambitious project to date. He launched himself on London.

At the Hyde Park end of Piccadilly he designed and built a new place of entertainment 'Winstanley's Waterworkes', which featured 'the greatest curiosities in waterworks, the like never performed by any'. The basis of the show was a series of moving tableaux in which trick effects were achieved with fountains and water spouts, and the mingling of fire and water. The show was an instantaneous hit with the nobility as well as the masses, and appears to have drawn the town for more than thirty years. The diarist John Evelyn is among those who refer to it in complimentary terms. The price of admission ranged from 2s. 6d. for a box to 6d. for the upper gallery.

Not the least of Winstanley's gifts was his sense of publicity. He was a born advertising man, and he ingeniously co-ordinated his various projects so that each would help to sell the others. At Littlebury you could buy engravings of the Waterworkes. (None of these, unfortunately, has survived.) At the Waterworkes you were invited to buy the playing-cards and engravings of celebrated English houses, including Winstanley's own at Littlebury. This print, as will be seen from the reproduction, carries an advertisement in two parts. In the left-hand panel Winstanley artfully promotes the general idea of noblemen having prints of their houses made at all.

He begins by saying that he gets very little profit himself out of this kind of thing, what with the cost of copper plates, travel expenses, and one thing and another. But, having seen most of the great houses of Europe or pictures of them, he thinks it a pity that the many English houses which are every bit as good are not nearly as well known because their owners are backward in having their beauties committed to paper. He conceives it to be his patriotic duty to bring together in a single volume as many prints of great English houses as possible. Such a volume would be a handy way of enabling not only the foreigner but also his own countrymen to obtain a rapid glimpse of the country's architectural treasures without having to spend time or money actually visiting the places.

In the right-hand panel of the advertisement Winstanley gets down to business:

> All Noble men and Gentlemen that please to have their Mansion Houses designed on Copper Plates to be printed for composing a volume of ye Prospects of Ye Principall Houses of England may have them done by Mr. Hen. Winstanley by way of subscription, that is to say, subscribing to pay five pounds at the delivering of a fair Coppy of their respective houses as large as this Plate; or tenn pounds for one as large as Royall paper will contain.

He would also be happy to supply as many prints at four-pence and sixpence as the proud owners might subsequently require, and when the volume of prints had been completed, each subscriber would receive a free copy. Below this second advertisement was a footnote:

You may have also any Prospect of your houses or any distannce Painted in Oyle of any size att a reasonable rate by me likewise.

It was a masterly example of the oblique approach. First, the disinterested introduction. Then the tariff, with the bait of the free copy of the bound volume thrown in. Finally, the throwaway tailpiece offering oil-paintings too if required, without a specific price being mentioned. The idea of the representative bound volume was extremely subtle—what man of quality could afford to have his house left out of such a collection?

But perhaps the shrewdest touch of all was that preamble which said, in effect: 'Of course I shall make nothing out of this myself, I shall be lucky if I cover expenses.' This is surely classic salesmanship.

Some time between 1685, when Charles II died, and 1688, when his successor James II was deposed by William of Orange, Winstanley published from his house at Littlebury a set of twenty-four engravings covering all the ground plans and prospects of Audley End. This collection, one of his major works, went on sale at the Waterworkes in London, a new reminder to all and sundry that if they wanted their houses recorded, Winstanley was their man. These prints—of which the British Museum has one of the very few complete sets still in existence—are not of much interest artistically, but historically they are valuable because they constitute the only complete record of Audley End in its original form. During the following century it was redesigned and largely rebuilt, and the new mansion which emerged bore little resemblance to the original and was about half its size.

Winstanley furnished these prints with no fewer than three dedications. The first, naturally enough, was to the reigning monarch James II, who now owned the place. The second, understandably, was to the Earl of Suffolk, whose grandfather had built it. The third was addressed to Sir Christopher Wren. Was this just another example of how Winstanley always overdid everything? Or, as one suspects, was it to exploit the name

value of the greatest architect of the day, then very much in
the public eye as he worked on the new St. Paul's Cathedral?

In 1695 Winstanley, now fifty-one, was at the height of his
fame. The Waterworkes had become an established part of the
London scene, and was patronized by every level of society.
The Wonders at Littlebury were practically a national institution. His prints and other publications were in wide circula-
tion. There were few people by this time who had not heard
of Henry Winstanley, formerly Clerk of the Works to Charles
II, practical eccentric, purposeful joker, fabulous showman.
His various enterprises had earned him a great deal of money
and he had invested some of this in one of the most profitable,
but risky, fields then available to a man with capital. He had
bought five ships. One had been lost on the Eddystone in
August. Another, the *Constant*, was due to reach Plymouth
before the end of the year.

He was in a London tavern when they brought him the news
that the *Constant* had been wrecked on the Eddystone, the
second wreck there in four weeks. Furious, he hurried to Plymouth, and like everyone who lost a ship at Eddystone, wanted
to know when something was going to be done about the reef.
They explained the position about the projected lighthouse.
There had been a royal authority for it nearly two years before,
but nothing had come of it. Now Trinity House had sold the
lease to a local man. But there was the question of finding an
architect willing to undertake the work.

An architect—so that was it. No one wanted the job. Impulsively Winstanley told the Mayor that he would build the
thing himself. He—Henry Winstanley of Littlebury in Essex,
Gent.—would build them their lighthouse.

This account of how Winstanley came to build the first
Eddystone lighthouse, though vouched for by only one
authority, is acceptable because it is entirely in character. Circumstances had brought him forcibly face to face with an issue
which from London might seem of minor importance but in
Plymouth was a smouldering grievance which burst into flame
every time the Eddystone wrecked another ship. Angered by
his financial loss, he would become heavily involved in the

Eddystone controversy and the interminable local arguments about whether it could or could not be done. It would not be long before a mind like Winstanley's began to turn over exciting new thoughts. They said it could not be done, did they?

What a challenge to a man famous for his mechanical ingenuity! What a tempting prospect for a showman who was also an exhibitionist! It would be natural for a man of Winstanley's temperament to think suddenly that this was the task for which he had been born. He had enjoyed fame and success for a long time. Now, almost by accident, he had been presented with a wonderful new world to conquer, a showman's dream.

This was something which would dwarf his previous achievements. It would blaze his name not across the country but across the world. It is easy to picture the pursing of the sensual lips, the gleam in the slanting sardonic eyes as the idea took root and shape, and in his mind he began to visualize the great lantern on the roof of the house at Littlebury transported magically to a tower in the middle of the ocean.

The taming of the Eddystone with a light would be Winstanley's greatest Waterworke, Winstanley's greatest Wonder. He had undertaken to do something which had never been done before. He was going to build a lighthouse on a wave-swept rock in the open sea.

It was a bold challenge. No one had yet attempted to build a rock lighthouse. The Tour de Cordouan, though a step in that direction, was not in the true sense a rock lighthouse. Admittedly the islet of Cordouan was some way from the mainland, difficult to approach, exposed to the open Atlantic, and submerged at high tide. But when the waters receded they left behind a considerable rock mass a thousand yards long, five hundred wide, and on one side of it there was at low water a usable beach. Building there was largely a matter of time and patience, and as we have seen, the tower took twenty-seven years to finish. The point is there was *room*. On the Eddystone there was no room.

In the whole of the three ridges which made up the Eddystone reef there was only one rock with a possible building surface

D

and high enough to remain exposed at high water. At its highest end it was about thirty feet broad, but it sloped sharply down at an angle of thirty degrees. On the other side it dropped almost vertically to the sea, though half-way down it receded to give the appearance of an open mouth. From the side its general outline was that of a right-angled triangle except for this mouth cutting deeply into its perpendicular end. A practicable building would require most of the broad upper surface of this rock, and this would leave very little space for the men and their building materials. The shelf provided by the lower jaw of the mouth at the vertical end of the rock would be the only place on which to make a landing.

This rock was the only possible choice, but its disadvantages were numerous. It was on the most westerly of the three ridges so that it caught the full force of the Atlantic swell. To land on the narrow shelf on its protected eastern side it was necessary to take a boat into the channel, only fifty feet wide, between this line of rocks and the central ridge of the reef—a funnel of heaving waters where the conflicting eddies were always at their worst. Landings were possible only at low water on the calmest days of summer.

Mention has been made of the tidal idiosyncrasies of the English Channel, where the rise and fall of the water overlaps instead of conforming to the turn of the tidal stream. This did not ease the problem of navigating small boats laden with heavy stone blocks a distance of fourteen miles from Plymouth to a reef which the largest boats went out of their way to avoid. There was only one way of doing this.

It was necessary to leave Plymouth immediately after high water, so that the ebb helped to take the boat clear of the Sound and into the open Channel. The boat was directed well to the east of Eddystone. The hope was that by the time it had reached the Channel some three hours later it would be able to catch the main tidal stream, which by then would have turned to flow from east to west. This current gave the only reasonable approach to the reef. And as the tidal water still had another three hours of ebb the reef could be reached with any luck at low water.

All other things being equal—and they seldom were—this

navigation plan would make it possible to land on the rocks for
two or three hours after a journey from Plymouth taking five
or six. In practice, this hardly ever happened. The essence
of the plan was timing, and a change of wind could wreck this
at any stage of the journey. There might be too much wind or
too little, and the boatmen would have to resort to oars. Even
if the winds and currents were amenable Eddystone was more
often than not unapproachable. And the three-hour difference
between the time the waters changed from flood to ebb and the
tidal current turned from east to west meant that if the boat
missed its appropriate current it would have to wait for several
hours until the next turn. In practice, the journey was much
more likely to take anything between eight and twelve hours. To
get to the reef at all was a major operation, without having then
to face the task of building a durable tower on a small, precarious, sloping, ocean-swept platform of barely penetrable
rock.

This was the task which, at the age of fifty-one, the jester of
Littlebury had impulsively undertaken. In its long history
the Atlantic can seldom have been challenged by so im-
probable an opponent. Four long summers later, when the
work had by some miraculous means been brought to a successful conclusion, Winstanley—in one of the regrettably fragmentary notes he made on the building—explained that it had
taken so long . . .

not for the greatness of the work but for the difficulty and danger
of getting backward and forward to the place, nothing being or
could be left there for the first two years but what was most
thoroughly affixed to the rock or the work at very extraordinary
charge. And though nothing could be attempted to be done but
in the summer season, yet the weather then at times would prove
so bad that for ten or fourteen days together the sea would be so
raging about these rocks—caused by outwinds and the running
of the ground seas coming from the main ocean—that though the
weather should seem to be most calm in other places, yet here it
would mount and fly more than two hundred foot as has been so
found since there was lodgment upon the place. And therefore
all our works were constantly buried at those times and exposed
to the mercy of the seas and no power was able to come near to

make good or help anything, as I have often experienced with my
workmen in a boat in great danger: only having the satisfaction
to see my work imperfectly at times as the seas fell from it at a
mile or two distance—and this at the prime of the year and no
wind or appearance of bad weather . . .

It was probably just as well that, in the winter of 1695–96,
as Winstanley the infinite enthusiast was preparing his plans for
the following spring, he did not have the slightest idea of what
he was really letting himself in for.

CHAPTER FIVE

Winstanley's Tower

In the early summer of 1696 Winstanley impatiently awaited a break in the weather. With luck the working season at Eddystone might last from July to October. But, as sceptical local boatmen never tired of reminding him, there would be days and even weeks when the weather, even in midsummer, made it impossible to get near the place, let alone land on it. They were into June now, and every day that went by was a precious thing lost. The first task of this first working summer was to prepare the foundation. His plan was to bore twelve holes in the rock and fix a heavy iron stanchion in each. These tall irons, embedded in the rock, would provide a firm skeleton around which the stone tower could be cemented. This was his plan for anchoring the tower to the rock. It was the first task of all, and he was anxious to get started.

By the end of June, when the first few trial journeys to the reef had been made, Winstanley knew that boring those twelve holes would not be the first, but the only task of that summer.

Twelve holes—it seemed simple enough. But the red gneiss was iron hard and reluctant to be pierced. You could chip into it by slashing laterally at its laminated flanks, along the direction of the grain, but if you struck against the grain as they had to do on its top surface the rock seemed impenetrable.

Tired out after a sea journey that could last anything up to eight hours, many of them devoted to hard rowing against the relentlessly punctual tidal currents, with only a precious hour or two of low water left in which to work, the brawniest men of Devon and Cornwall would seize their picks and unloose them on the unyielding gneiss. Twelve holes—it was ridiculous. It was an affront to the pride of these hand-picked labourers that they could make so small an impression.

Cheered on by their eccentric leader, and gradually working

up an insensate hatred of the stubborn rock, the men would swing their picks harder and higher. Savagely they would strike at the damnable surface, determined to pierce it, punish it, hurt it for the trouble it was causing them. Sometimes one of them would swing a little too high and overbalance on the treacherous sloping surface and fall backwards on the sharp rocks below. Often a wave would come swirling over the reef just as a man was at full stretch and about to strike, and catching him off balance it would sweep him off his feet. Even if the waves were inconsiderable there were always great fountains of spray, and you could not be on the rock for many minutes without being soaked.

It was a common occurrence for a pick to fly out of a man's hand because the handle had become too wet to grip. They would take spare picks, and as soon as one had been blunted it would be replaced by another newly sharpened. But these picks were a pitifully impotent weapon with which to break the ageless crust of Eddystone. Twelve holes. July passed and August. A few rough penetrations were all that they had to show for it. Twelve holes.

There were times when the outward journey took many hours owing to a change of wind, and then the currents were wrong, and only by exhausting oarsmanship could they get there at all. There were times when, having arrived, they could not land. And others when a return to Plymouth was impossible and they had to make for one of the Cornish fishing villages— Looe, Polperro, Fowey—or ride out a storm in the open sea.

For Winstanley, Littlebury (which his wife was looking after in his absence) and the Water Theatre in London were by this time something belonging to a previous existence. Twelve holes—that was all that mattered now. He must drive twelve deep holes in this red rock by autumn.

It needed all his charm and persuasiveness and genial sense of humour to hold his work parties together. The journeys to the rock could never be less than extremely uncomfortable, and often they were highly dangerous. As soon as they arrived, they had to go to work on a frustrating task that for a long time seemed impossible, and all the time they had to endure being drenched to the skin. There was always uncertainty about the return journey: the weather changed so quickly out there, you never knew whether you would see your bed in Plymouth for three days or more, or when you would find yourself drying out on some remote beach up the coast. Once back in Plymouth, there were frustrating days when the wind blew hard and the boatmen shook their heads and said that there was no hope of getting out to the rock that day, or the next, or the one after that. These must have been the most infuriating times of all for Winstanley, for then the sceptics would come into their own. They had known all along that the project was impossible. It was madness to go on; they had heard from the men about the difficulty of penetrating the rock with picks; it was all over the town; why did he not give up now and save himself a deal of trouble? He would have to endure much talk of this kind. And all the time the summer was wasting away. The iron stanchions were ready; they had been ready for some time. All that he needed was the twelve holes in which they were to be fixed. Just twelve holes. Twelve holes . . .

Then the weather would clear and immediately after high tide the boats would move into the Sound, and by now they had done it so often that they were getting better at it. They were more used to the tides and currents and winds, so less time was lost on the way—unless the weather happened to play one of its more capricious tricks.

Increasingly they were beginning to think of Eddystone as the only work they had ever done. Had there been a life before Eddystone? Imperceptibly it became a little easier. They were cleverer at landing. Even the extremest landlubbers among them had subconsciously turned into passable spare seamen. Working on the slippery slanting rock was not quite as awkward as it had been: there was a knack to it: it was all a question of balance and being used to it. They were better at it now, at long last their perseverance was beginning to show results. Once an impression had been made, once the rock had been proved to be vulnerable after all and twelve holes undeniably began to appear as a result of these weeks of toil, the prospect was not so bad. You could work on those holes. They were there. They were definite. They existed. You could deepen them. And working with Mr. Winstanley had its compensations. He was mad, of course, quite mad, but good company. Very amusing with those conjuring tricks of his . . .

In the end they beat the weather by a few days. It was late October when they knew that they had won, and the twelve great irons were taken out in relays to be scorched with molten lead into the holes that with such infinite effort had been prepared for them. It was a happy day when, pulling hard on their oars, they looked back for the last time that season on the reef. The Atlantic, as always, was pounding the reef and raising clouds of spray. With the tide coming in fast it seemed that they had almost left it too late to cast off for Plymouth. But now there was something else to look at, something heartening. Twelve iron shafts pierced deeply into the back of the tallest rock, spikes which the sea and the rock could not dislodge.

They had harpooned the monster and left it to bleed and weaken. Next summer they would return for the kill.

The second working season began well. There had been several months in which to recover from the rigours of the first year's work. They knew now what they were up against and how better to cope with the journeys to and from the reef. It was good to have finished with the tedious and unrewarding preliminaries and to be getting on with the actual building. Soon they would have something to show for all their trouble.

During the winter, too, public interest in the Eddystone enterprise had been steadily growing. No project involving Henry Winstanley could remain a secret. Eddystone was becoming a household word, and the whole country was eager to know what would happen. This also was heartening.

Winstanley's first design envisaged a circular tower consisting of three sections of roughly equal height: first a solid stone base, above it a hollow stone section containing a storeroom and a living-room, and above this a wooden superstructure which would embrace the lantern and a small kitchen-cum-service room just below it.

In the very brief building notes which he wrote later, Winstanley makes no mention of any special steps taken to secure the base to the sloping surface of the rock other than the planting of the twelve iron supports. It can therefore be assumed that he relied entirely on these. The stones, one of the local granites, would have to be pre-fabricated in Plymouth and cut to allow for the slope. They were then cemented on to the rock and around the irons in such a way that these supports would provide the base with a metal bone-structure.

Transferring the heavy stones from an undulating small boat to the reef was a tricky business, but the block and tackle could be operated on a reef as well as anywhere else, and these men were becoming particularly expert in doing things on reefs. The work was going well in this summer of 1697 when a new hazard threatened it—a hazard which for once could not be blamed on the weather or the ocean.

England was at war with France. It was the first of those protracted wars in which England and her continental allies resisted the threatened domination of Europe by the powerful and ambitious Louis XIV. It had already lasted several years, and that very autumn, as it happened, it was due to be brought to a temporary and uneasy halt. But that was not to be until September, and though there was already some vague talk of peace, in June the war was still very much in progress. Because of this the Admiralty, which for obvious reasons was deeply interested in the Eddystone project, was providing Winstanley with the protection of a warship on days when he was working at the reef.

The ship entrusted with this duty, which it doubtless found tedious and boring, was H.M.S. *Terrible*, commanded by Captain Timothy Bridge. One morning in late June the *Terrible* failed to put in an appearance. When in due course the builders saw a warship approaching they assumed that another must have been detailed in its place. It was not until it had come in close and fired some playful rounds at the reef that they realized that it was a French privateer. The workmen were allowed to remain, but Winstanley himself was seized and carried off to France.

The Admiralty lost no time in trying to make amends for its lapse. An urgent note was sent to the French authorities demanding the release of Winstanley. A strong note was addressed to the senior naval officer in Plymouth, Commissioner St. Loe, demanding an explanation. An Admiralty minute dated 28 June, 1697 reads:

Resolved that Commissioner St. Loe be directed to give an account of how it happened that the workemen on the Eddystone were soe ill protected as that the Engineer was taken and carried to ffrance by a small ffrench challoope.

Perhaps not surprisingly, the errant Captain Bridge made no mention of the incident in the log of H.M.S. *Terrible*.

The behaviour of the French king was exemplary. As soon as he heard what had happened Louis ordered the release of Winstanley and the punishment of the officer who had captured him, remarking that he 'was at war with England not with humanity', and adding that a lighthouse on the Eddystone was as important to France as it was to England. He then sent for Winstanley and apologized to him. It comes as no surprise to learn that Winstanley, who had some experience of endearing himself to monarchs, had his usual success with Louis, who was fascinated by the fast-talking Englishman and his endless flow of ideas: so much so that he tried to persuade him to return to Paris and work for him. Within less than a fortnight Winstanley was back in England, something of a hero, and enriched by a number of costly presents from Louis XIV to compensate him for being inconvenienced. After this there could not possibly be anyone in the country who did not know about Winstanley and his Eddystone lighthouse. With all his flair for publicity he could not have done better if he had planned the whole thing himself.

But two precious weeks had been wasted. It was now the middle of July. Winstanley was determined that the first phase of the building, the solid stone base, should be completed by the end of that working season. He called on his men for an extra effort to make up for the time that had been lost.

It was a laborious business. In his own words 'we had great trouble to take off and land so many materials, and be forced to secure all things as aforesaid every night and time we left work, or return them again in the boats'. As the materials consisted in the main of great blocks of granite, his point can be appreciated. The rowing would be harder than ever. Hoisting the great blocks on to the reef was a dangerous and lengthy proceeding. Difficult enough if it went smoothly, it could always be undone by an unexpected wave at the wrong moment. At this early stage the lifting and placing of every single stone was a major operation. It could take the whole of one of the short working sessions snatched between tides to set two or three. There was always the dilemma of deciding, with one eye on a sea growing visibly rougher, whether to risk one more stone or to stop then, make certain that the loose stones and other materials to be left overnight were absolutely secured, and cast off for home quickly while the going was good.

It was better when the structure had risen above the level of the rock and they had a flat platform on which to work instead of a slope. Once this stage had been reached they could work a little faster, and this gave them new heart. Even on calm days the spray still soaked them and made every working session uncomfortable, and when the sea turned suddenly and inexplicably rough, as it so often did at Eddystone, the waves could turn discomfort into misery. But they were slowly but surely wearing down their opposition. Under Winstanley's leadership their own attrition was becoming as relentless as that of their tireless opponent the ocean. It was a wonderful moment when, in the deteriorating weather of autumn, the last stone of the base was lowered into place. In spite of the June interruption, the work was up to schedule. To show for the second summer's work they had what Winstanley described as 'a solid body or kind of round pillar twelve foot high and fourteen foot diameter'. This was the turning-point.

The third working summer began in a mood of high optimism and growing public excitement. The lighthouse had fired popular imagination throughout the country. Its progress was being followed everywhere. King William had shown a close personal interest in it, and Winstanley was confidently telling everyone that he would finish that year; Eddystone would be showing a light next winter. Interest was growing all the time. Plymouth had become a grandstand for the Greatest Show On Earth. It was a situation after Winstanley's heart.

He had decided during the winter that the base of the tower needed to be bigger, and had re-designed the rest of the building in proportion. His first action, as soon as it was fit to go out to the reef, was to enlarge the base constructed the previous summer. The diameter was increased from fourteen to sixteen feet: the height from twelve feet to eighteen.

Progress was rapid. Before many weeks had passed they had finished the base and were working on the upper stone section of the tower. This was to be polygonal in shape and would consist of a store-room and above it a living apartment, which the builder grandly named the State Room.

Winstanley pressed his men to greater efforts, for a transformation in the working pattern was at hand which must please them as much as him. Once the walls of this habitable part of the tower had reached a substantial height they would provide enough shelter for working parties to live on the spot, and for larger quantities of building materials to be stored there. The saving in time would be considerable. It would be wonderful to be able to reduce the number of journeys to and from Plymouth, wonderful to be no longer entirely at the mercy of tides and winds, wonderful to eliminate those infuriating interruptions when the weather made it impossible to approach the reef. Progress would be so much more constant. This was why Winstanley was so confident that by next winter there would be a light on the Eddystone. By midsummer he considered the building sufficiently advanced to put the new system into operation.

The Eddystone, however, and its ally the Atlantic were not yet beaten. As if to punish him for this new insolence, on the first night that Winstanley and his workmen chose to set up their temporary home at the reef, a typical Eddystone storm blew up from nowhere to shatter the peace of a warm June night: a night when a sleep under the stars with the Cormorants, the Shags, the Great Black-backs, and the soothing rumble of the waves for company must have seemed a good end to a hard day's work; and certainly a more than welcome change from a fatiguing sail back to Plymouth followed by a return journey early the next day. This was how Winstanley described it:

> We ventured to lodge there soon after midsummer for greater dispatch of this work, but the first night the weather came bad and so continued, that it was eleven days before any boat could come near us again, and not being acquainted with the height of the

seas rising, we were nearly all ye time neer drowned with wet and all our provisions in as bad a condition, though we worked night and day as much as possible to make shelter for ourselves. In this storm we lost some of our materials although we did what we could to save them. But the boat then returning we all left the house to be refreshed on shore, and as soon as the weather did permitt, we returned again. . . .

It was a salutary reminder that the Eddystone could never be taken for granted. Even in midsummer a gale could castigate it for eleven days and nights.

This inauspicious beginning to the new phase of living at the reef was the last serious interruption. With the working party re-established there progress was methodical and steady. The stone tower was completed. One by one the pre-fabricated components of the superstructure were brought out by boat and fixed into position—the stairways; the wooden balustrade for the open gallery and other external and internal fittings; the umbrella-shaped kitchen; the lantern. In a final burst of late-Renaissance *joie de vivre* Winstanley—who could never resist the impulse to be fancy and never knew when to stop—finished the whole thing off with a splendidly elegant but imprudently heavy wrought-iron bracket to support the weather vane.

On 14 November, 1698 Henry Winstanley climbed up to the lantern and lit a number of tallow candles.

The news spread fast. As the first fishermen began to come in with the incredible report that the Eddystone was showing a light the people poured out of their homes to see it. In Plymouth they raced up to the Hoe, as they always did when something exciting was happening, and they peered through the darkness, trying to pick up the light with the aid of telescopes. Elsewhere along the coast they flocked to the beaches and to the cliff-tops. There was a light on the Eddystone. Winstanley had done it. Winstanley had achieved the impossible. He had lit the Eddystone. It was marvellous and not quite believable. Some of them piled into boats and sailed or rowed out into the Sound in the hope of spotting the light with the naked eye, and others made for Rame Head, the headland closest to the reef—it ought to be possible to see the light from there.

The syndicate who had put up the money (it included Winstanley himself, who had invested £5,000 in it) was particularly happy. The light meant that they could now start collecting dues. A light on the Eddystone—it was incredible. To these western English, to whom seafaring was life itself and the Eddystone a hereditary curse they had lived with for generations, it was hard to take in the news that the forlorn effort of the strange Mr. Winstanley had actually succeeded. The impact of the news was stunning. As stunning as a later generation would have found a front page informing it that the Great Barnum had sent the first rocket to the moon.

But there was one category of men who marvelled more profoundly than the others, whose astonishment on those first few nights was mingled with reverence and humility and tears. To the common sailors—some making for Plymouth for the first time, others after an absence of months or years—the first sight of the yellow glare of Winstanley's tallow candles shining above the breakers far from the land was something more than a wondrous phenomenon. To these simple men, practising the most perilous of trades, it was a miraculous act of Providence.

The only persons who were prevented from enjoying Winstanley's triumph and joining in the general celebrations were Winstanley himself and the handful of men who had been with him at the end. Owing to continuous rough seas it was five weeks before a boat could approach the Eddystone to pick them up. At least he had an unrivalled opportunity to observe the behaviour of his creation under battle conditions.

> We put up the light [wrote Winstanley] on the 14th of November, 1698. Which being so late in the year it was three days before Christmas before we had a relief to get ashore again, and were almost at the last extremity for want of provisions, but by good providence then two boats came with provisions and the family that was to take care of the light, and so ended this year's work.

Early the following spring, Winstanley took advantage of the first spell of calm weather to visit the Eddystone and discover how the lighthouse had stood up to its baptismal winter. What he found was disturbing. The winter seas, endlessly hammering, endlessly probing for a weakness had found one. The cement.

The conditions in which the base of the tower had had to be constructed—the impossibility of sheltering the work from the waves and the spray—had prevented the cement from setting properly. Relentlessly the salt-water had exposed this weakness and the pointing of the stonework was in very bad repair. On top of this the keepers had hair-raising stories of what they had endured during the winter: how the tower shuddered frighteningly under the blows of the waves, how the lantern itself was frequently underwater in high seas, how waves sometimes swept up the building and formed a great spout many feet above it. The keepers did not underplay what they had to tell, and Winstanley—himself no mean story-teller—would no doubt take some of it with a pinch of salt. But what he saw and heard was enough to convince him that his work was not yet finished. He made a quick and courageous decision. The entire building was to be strengthened and enlarged.

As soon as he had re-designed the components for the new superstructure and instructed those who were to make them, he left for the Eddystone. In effect what he was about to do was to encase the whole of the first tower in a new one. The base was increased by 4 feet all round to a diameter of 24 feet, and heightened by 2 feet, which meant that the solid part of the tower was now 20 feet high. To overcome the difficulty with the cement, all the jointings of the base, which received the main shock of the waves, were covered with bands of iron. The upper half of the stone tower was similarly encased to give it the same diameter as the new base, and it was greatly increased in height. It was now 60 feet from the lowest part of the foundation to the open gallery, as against the 35 feet it had been in the first building.

The new superstructure was on similar lines to the first, but larger and stronger, and in its vaguely telescopic design less top-heavy. The extra dimensions allowed for a much larger 'umbrella' room above the open gallery, an additional small room between this and the lantern, and an upper gallery around the lantern, which was taller than its predecessor. The overall height from base to weather vane was now 120 feet as against the 80 of the original building.

The work was completed during the summer of 1699—the

fourth summer of work at the rock—and the astonishing result was before very long a familiar sight to the public at large. For Winstanley, true to form, lost no time in preparing a large-scale drawing of his creation and selling copies of it at the Water Theatre in London and at his house in Littlebury as fast as the engravers could turn out prints. The picture was an immediate best-seller, and remained one for many years. Sixty years after Winstanley's death engravers were still publishing new editions. In addition, he built large models of the lighthouse in the garden at Littlebury and at the Water Theatre, and these drew large crowds to both places.

Winstanley's drawing of the completed lighthouse is more than a guide to the building. It is a revealing guide to the man who built it. He completed the picture with these descriptive notes on the various parts of the building.

At the bottom of the lighthouse on the right:

An engine crane that parts at joints to be taken off when not in use, the rest being fastened to the side of the house to save it in time of storms, and it is to be made use of to help landing on the rock, which without is very difficult.

Above this crane:

A gallery to take in goods and provisions from the boat to the store-room.

Winstanley sketched himself fishing from his gallery. The window to the left of its roof is:

The window of a very fine bedchamber with a chimney and closet, the room being richly gilded and painted and the outside shutters very strongly barred.

The apartment immediately above the bedchamber and extending as high as the gallery was:

The State Room, being 10 square 19 foot wide, and 12 foot high, very well carved and painted, with a chimney and 2 closets, and 2 sash windows with strong shutters to bar and bolt.

Winstanley's descriptive idiom here would not disgrace a modern house agent.

Above the State Room:

The Airry or open Gallery where is conveniency to crane up goods and a great leaden cistern to hold the rainwater that falls from upper roofs in pipes and to let the sea pass through in times of storms.

The umbrella-shaped room above the Gallery:

The kitchen where is a large chimney, oven, dressers, and table, with a large closet and a large standing bed.

The small hexagonal room above it:

A bedchamber with 2 cabbin beds and all conveniences for a dining room with large lockers to hold a great store of candles for lights.

Above this the lantern:

The lanthorn that holds the lights is 8 square, 11 foot diameter 15 foot high in the upright wall: having 8 great glass windows, and ground plates for squares, and conveniency to burn 60 candles at a time besides a great hanging lamp. There is door to go into the gallery that is all round, to cleanse the glass of the lanthorn, which is often dim'd by salt water that washeth it in storms.

To the left of the 'umbrella' room:

A gallery to go out to put the ensign or make a signal.

The container suspended from it on a chain:

Is a vessel to let float on the water to take in small things from a boat on the west side of the rock when there is no landing on the other side.

The crane at the same level on the right of the house:

Is a large standing crane to take things at a distance when no boats can come near the rock.

Alongside it:

Is a small iron turning crane to take things into the Airry or the store room below.

But nothing illustrates Winstanley's quality of purposeful whimsy so much as the six graceful candlesticks bracketed to

E

the *outside* of the lantern. This was how he described and justified them:

> Great wooden candlesticks for ornament; but the irons that bears them is very useful to stay a ladder to clear the glass.

There was a final masterly touch. Winstanley had not forgotten his rough handling by the French privateer two years previously. The lighthouse must be equipped to resist invasion. Projecting downwards from the rail of the gallery on the right-hand side of the sketch is a chute. Winstanley described it as:

> A moving engine trough to cast down stones to defend the landing place in case of need.

Truly he had thought of everything.

As usual, he could not resist a final excess of decoration. Inscriptions or decorative devices were added to almost every flat surface available. Below the lantern were stars and the inscription 'Anno Dom 1699'; below this the date again and reference to the reign of William III; around the ten-sided upper part of the tower, impressions of the sun and the moon and various inscriptions: '*Post Tenebras Lux*', '*In Salutem Omnium*', '*Pax In Bello*', 'Glory Be to God'. Finally, above the main entrance door, an engraved tablet placed beyond any doubt, if doubt there could possibly be, that the lighthouse had been designed and constructed by Winstanley. It was in Latin: HANC PHARON DESIGNAVIT ET STRUXIT H. WINSTANLY DE LITTLEBURY IN COM. ESSEX GENT ANNO DOM 1699.

It will be observed that one non-Latin word crept into this otherwise impeccably Roman statement: the four-letter word that was always so precious to Winstanley: GENT.

The enlarged lighthouse came triumphantly through its first winter. Sailors were delighted with the increased range resulting from the extra height. For two years, now, no ship had been lost on the Eddystone. A third year passed without the loss of a single ship, and the rebuilt tower had emerged from its second winter test with only a fraction of the wear and tear suffered by its predecessor: a working party could put this right

in a few days. But now that the novelty was beginning to wear
off (except for seamen, who continued to regard the lighthouse
with reverent wonder) sceptical voices were heard again on
shore.

How long could the tower survive? Surely all that over-
elaboration of the external fittings was asking for trouble?
That they were still there simply meant that they had yet to
experience the Atlantic breakers at their worst. Was not the
superstructure far too cumbersome and top-heavy? And too
flimsily attached to the stone tower? Were there not too many
excrescences for the waves to tear at? Was not the whole thing
far too fancy?

These were the questions that people were beginning to ask.
The more perceptive critics were also worried by the polygonal
form of the greater part of the tower. It was surely a mistake
to present flat surfaces to the waves? Nor did the spine-chilling
tales told by the keepers do anything to dispel these doubts.
Whenever a relief was carried out a new crop of fearsome tales
came ashore with the keepers. After a few drinks there was
no limit to the size of the waves a man could distinctly remember having experienced the week before last; waves, he
would tell his goggle-eyed tavern audience, twice as high as the
lighthouse itself; waves that buried the lantern for seconds on
end. In a storm the house rocked so badly that crockery would
be shaken off the table, and sometimes men were sea-sick.
There was a favourite story that on one occasion a six-oared
rowing-boat, driven on the reef during a gale, had been lifted
clean through the open gallery of the lighthouse on a great
wave. A new mythology of dangerous living had come into
being.

It is more than likely that Plymouth had had its fill of Henry
Winstanley by this time. It was deeply grateful to him, of
course, for a marvellous achievement. But his vanity, his
metropolitan self-assurance, his love of display and decoration
and extravagance, his lively humour, his gusto, and his gay
temperament reflected too closely the *zeitgeist* of the Restoration. Plymouth was a dour city where Puritanism died hard.
Its people were for the most part rugged, sabbatarian, grimly
Nonconformist. Half a century after the Civil War, Plymouth

was still allergic to cavaliers. They would find it easy to disapprove of many of Winstanley's attitudes, and in time begin to persuade themselves that these traits which they despised had led him to spoil a job that should have been considered only in the most severely practical terms. At the end of each summer it became a subject of morbid speculation whether the lighthouse would last another winter. Winstanley, aware of this growing body of gloomy sceptics, was goaded into boasting publicly that he had one crowning wish in life—to be in his beloved lighthouse during 'the greatest storm that ever was'.

Meanwhile the lighthouse emerged unscathed from its fourth winter, though it did have to face a crisis that had nothing to do with the weather, caused Winstanley a great deal of trouble and anxiety, and brought fame of a sort to a humble Plymouth boatman named James Bound. As he was about to leave for the Eddystone with urgently needed supplies of candles and food, Bound was seized by a Navy press-gang.

'Mr. Winstanley', wrote the Trinity House agent in his letter of protest to the Lord High Admiral, 'is under no small trouble to find his only man taken from him upon whom was all his dependence in landing at the house where nobody else could or would venture.' The release of Bound was demanded, and also future protection against the press-gangs. Both demands were acceded to. James Bound, the only man who dared face the Eddystone in rough weather, was eventually able to deliver his food and candles to the keepers, who by that time were in desperate need of both.

In the spring William III died and was succeeded by Queen Anne. The war with France was resumed, the pretext being the succession to the Spanish Throne, the cause the inevitability of a final showdown with Europe's greatest military power and the unsatisfied ambition of its ruler, Louis XIV. John Churchill, Duke of Marlborough, took command of the Allied Armies and embarked on the campaign that was to establish him as one of the greatest of generals. His wife Sarah took command of the Queen and embarked on that control of her Court that was to establish her as one of the most formidable *éminences grises* of all time.

In November 1703—by which time Marlborough was back

in England after his preliminary success against the fortresses of
the Meuse and Lower Rhine—Winstanley returned to Plymouth to organize some urgent repairs to the Eddystone, which,
from the point of view of the British and Dutch Navies, would
be contributing its own usefulness to the waging of the new war
with France.

As usual there was some speculation in Plymouth whether
the Eddystone would survive another winter—which would be
its sixth. As usual, Winstanley repeated his now well-known re-
tort that he asked nothing better than to be inside it during 'the
greatest storm that ever was'.

Meanwhile the repairs to the lighthouse were urgent. He
ordered the boat to stand by, ready to take him and a party of
workmen to the reef as soon as the weather allowed.

CHAPTER SIX

The Great Storm

IT was not just a storm. It was The Storm. The Great
Storm. The greatest recorded storm in British history, the
only known occasion on which the British Islands have
been struck in their entirety by the equivalent of the Florida
hurricane, the West African tornado, the China Sea typhoon.
This is known because that diligent journalist Daniel Defoe
lived through it. There had been the Great Plague, there had
been the Great Fire. Now it was the Great Storm. Defoe, who
had fully chronicled the two earlier calamities, was provided with
the opportunity to complete a memorable trilogy of disaster.

From his own experience in London, and the reports that
came to him during the nation-wide investigation he carried out
afterwards, Defoe was able to build up a composite picture
which seems to establish beyond reasonable doubt that this was
the most devastating tempest ever recorded in this country.

The high fury of the storm was concentrated into a few hours
between midnight and dawn of the night of 26/27 November,
1703. It swept the whole country, with its centre in the neighbourhood of Liverpool. Everywhere south of this there was
considerable damage, but it was below a line roughly between
Bristol and London that devastation was absolute. What added
to the terror of these few hours was that the storm was not a
sudden limited visitation. It came at the end of a solid fortnight
of Atlantic gales so violent that people were saying there had
been nothing like them in memory. So that when, after the
briefest lull, this ultimate fury was unloosed, it was as though an
unimaginable and impossible climax had been piled on an
ordeal that seemed already to have exhausted climactic possibility.

One effect of this fortnight of storm had been to fill the
anchorages and roadsteads of Britain with unprecedented

concentrations of shipping. Outside every port ships in their
hundreds were waiting for the gales to abate. The reason was
that those which had been homeward-bound from the west had
been driven in so fast by the high winds that they had arrived
many days early, while scores of outward-bound ships had been
forced to turn back and make for the nearest anchorage. In
gales of this intensity harbours had to be avoided as much as
the open sea. It was only in the roadsteads outside that sailing-
ships could hope to ride out such weather. By the end of two
weeks ships of every shape and size crowded the anchorages of
every port in the country.

On Thursday, 25 November there was at last the lull for
which everyone had been waiting. On sea and on land there
was that wave of relief which always follows a period of exceptional gales. Fretful ships' masters sniffed the declining
winds and decided that they could sail the next day or the day
after. On land men exchanged storm experiences and looked
forward to a night in bed without the roof rattling. It had been
a hard two weeks, but now it was over.

In Plymouth Henry Winstanley summoned his working
party and told them that they would be going out to the Eddystone the following morning to carry out those repairs for which
they had been standing by for many days, repairs which he
knew would be more urgently necessary after the recent gales.
Early in the morning of Friday, 26 November, Winstanley, now
a man of fifty-nine, sailed with his workmen from the Barbican
Steps and headed into Plymouth Sound. The sea was still
quite rough, and there were some who advised against the
journey. But Winstanley was determined to go, and he landed
on the reef in the afternoon.

It continued calm during the afternoon and the early evening of that Friday. Most people were in bed when, shortly
before midnight, the wind veered to the south-west and blew up
again with startling suddenness to an intensity beyond anything
any of them could have imagined possible. There was no
thunder, no rain, and except in a number of country places
which afterwards reported 'strange fires and lights' very little
lightning. There was just wind. Wind which quickly soared
from a scream to a high, sustained, cataclysmic roar of thunder.

It was this continuous wind-roar, with the volume and intensity of thunder, yet to the more objective observers definitely not thunder, which gave to the next few hours their uniquely numbing terror. This wind-roar was more frightening than the nightmare dangers it created, because it was strange and beyond known experience, and because it never abated throughout the night. To the simple it was the Day of Judgment, and they fell to their knees gibbering, or if they were in bed they cowered under the bedclothes like children. It was the more frightening, too, because it happened at the time when the new moon was due, and it had to be endured in a night of total blackness.

All over southern England every town and village became enveloped in a hail of flying slates and tiles. The more fragile buildings were blasted into rubble, the more solid ones stripped into skeletons. People who wished to escape the horror of disintegrating homes were deterred from doing so by the flying debris they would have to face if they went outside. Death in their beds or by their hearths seemed a lesser evil.

So great was the power of this wind that the heaviest tiles flew, not with the curving trajectory that would be normal, but straight, and they struck with such force that even on hard ground they buried themselves from five to eight inches.

A monotonously regular feature of the storm in the towns and in the country was the collapse of chimney-stacks, which came crashing down on houses, either cutting through them like cheese or destroying them entirely. Trees were uprooted or snapped off in thousands, and the heaviest oaks were as helpless as the lightest fruit-trees.

In Stowmarket they were rather proud of the strong new hundred-foot spire that had recently been built on their church in place of one that had grown weak with time. In the early stages of the storm this new spire was bodily overturned by the wind, and crashed down across the church.

In London St. James's Palace was damaged by falling chimney-stacks, and the Queen had to take refuge in a cellar. The guard-house at Whitehall was also damaged by falling masonry and eight soldiers of the guard injured. Westminster Abbey was badly damaged, as were six Oxford college towers.

Everywhere men and animals caught in the open were lifted off their feet and deposited in heaps some yards away, one man being carried six yards. Panic-stricken birds were blasted out of the air against buildings or to the ground to die in heaps.

An experience common to the whole of the southern half of the country was the wholesale stripping of the lead linings of church roofs. Often these great heavy sheets of lead were rolled up like parchment, sometimes they were removed bodily and carried, like flying carpets, many yards from the building they had formerly covered. Windmills suffered particularly. In one country village a small thatched house was lifted off the ground and deposited intact some yards from its original position.

A special horror was reserved for the West Country, where the wind played havoc with the tides. The rich commercial port of Bristol lost £150,000 of goods as a result of the flooding of warehouses and stores near the harbour. The wind blowing directly up the estuary of the Severn, lifted its waters into a tidal wave eight feet higher than the highest ever recorded. The banks were smashed and miles of countryside flooded. Scores of buildings were washed away, and in one district alone 15,000 sheep were drowned.

A victim of one of the numberless falling chimney-stacks was the Bishop of Bath and Wells, who was found crushed to death by one of them. He lay in his dressing-gown near the door of his bedroom, apparently caught in the act of trying to get away. His wife was still in bed, buried under many tons of rubble.

As always in a catastrophe on this scale, there were stories of stubborn calm and miraculous escapes. One Londoner slept soundly through the whole thing and was surprised to find no roof over his head when he woke up in the morning. A notary named Simpson, whose house was in Cheapside, was begged by his family to leave with them. Simpson would not hear of it and went back to sleep. His family cowered miserably in the cellar for an hour, then made another effort to persuade him to leave. He assured them that he could hear nothing that alarmed him, and told them to leave him alone. They left the house then, and were barely clear before it collapsed.

There were many escape stories. A man in Holborn who

had slept soundly through the night woke up to find himself staring at the open sky. A thin plank, sagging ominously under a great weight of debris, was directly above his head. He quickly got out of bed and almost immediately the wood cracked and the rubble crashed down where his head had been a few seconds before.

John Hanson, Registrar of Eton, who was in London on business, was spending the night at the Bell-Savage Inn on Ludgate Hill. He was asleep in a first-floor bedroom when the chimney-stack drove through the roof, the two upper storeys of the building, and finally the floor on which he was sleeping. His bed crashed through to the ground floor and made a perfect landing without Hanson sustaining anything worse than mild shock, though an avalanche of masonry was streaming through the gaps torn by the collapsed chimneys.

A different effect of the storm was reported by the vicar of a village near Oxford. The vicar, one of many who replied to Defoe's request for first-hand accounts, began with a modest statement to the effect that the wind had done 'no great harm, only in untiling houses, blowing down a chimney or two, without any person hurt, and a few trees'. But something strange had happened the previous afternoon. A man had come running to him in a state of considerable fright, begging him to go and look at a 'pillar in the air' which was moving across an adjacent field.

The vicar went and what he saw was 'a spout marching directly with the wind'. He could only compare its appearance to 'the trunk of an elephant, only much bigger'. It was extended to a great length, and swept the ground as it went, leaving behind it a mark. It crossed a field and meeting an isolated oak standing in the middle of the field 'snapped the body of it asunder'. Then, crossing a road, it sucked up the water in the ruts and ditches, wrecked an old barn and swirled its thatched roof into a cloud of straw particles, and finally disappeared behind a crest, so that its course could no longer be observed. But it was learned soon after that a man in the neighbouring parish had been lifted off his feet and knocked unconscious, but when he came round had no idea of what had hit him.

This cyclone is an indication of the extent to which this storm differed in kind from anything normally experienced in the British Isles. There was a tailpiece to the vicar's story. On the morning after the storm they found a tall elm which had been 'perfectly twisted round' but was still standing, 'the root a little loosened, but not torn up'.

This was one of the stranger happenings. Most of the reports that came in were grimly repetitive. Almost everyone told of shredded houses, collapsing chimney-stacks, flooded rivers, flying tiles, lead roofing that had been rolled up like paper or torn bodily from the tops of churches, spires that had been blown down or badly damaged, windmills overturned, people buried in rubble and blown off their feet, and trees ripped up in their thousands.

That was the story on land. At sea and in the river mouths it was, if anything, worse. The huge congestion of shipping that had resulted from the gales of the previous fortnight produced its comparably huge chaos when the new storm broke. Ships were driven helplessly against each other and into the stone quays which they had tried to avoid by moving out into the roadsteads. Masts were snapped off like twigs, and the wounded hulls either capsized or were driven uncontrollably to the open sea. In the river conditions were indescribable. In the horse-shoe bends they smashed against the banks and over them in heaps, the prow of one driving through the beam of another. Scores of them ended up on their sides acting as supports for others that had come to rest almost vertically. Many vessels were ground to matchwood, and others were swept over flooded river banks into the fields beyond, in some cases smashing into buildings and wrecking them.

The peak of this tempest was in the darkest hours of the early morning between 2 a.m. and 5 a.m., and during this time the wind veered from south-west to west and then to north-west and back to west: as though methodically spraying its target like some cosmic machine-gun, determined that none should escape: and as it began to fall back to the west and then the south-west, it began to lose its power, and by eight that morning it was all over.

The final reckoning made harsh reading. Defoe could preface it with the nonchalant warning that: 'Those towns who only had their houses untiled, their barns and hovels levelled with the ground, and the like, will find very little notice taken of them in this account.'

In all more than eight hundred dwelling-houses had been completely destroyed, apart from the many thousands severely damaged. More than a thousand country mansions had been damaged by the collapse of chimney-stacks. At least four hundred windmills were blown down. At least a hundred churches had their roof linings stripped, seven spires were entirely blown down and many more damaged. It was established that 123 people lost their lives, though many more could be presumed to have been buried in the ruins and never officially accounted for. The loss of ships was finally thought to be in the neighbourhood of a hundred and fifty, and no fewer than eight thousand sailors were said to have died that night.

As for the number of trees destroyed, all that can be said is that it ran into hundreds of thousands. In the course of a tour of parts of Kent which Defoe made shortly afterwards he started counting them conscientiously, but when he reached seventeen thousand he gave up: it seemed pointless and wearisome to go on. He had covered only a part of one county, and there were others much more thickly wooded. He established, however, that twenty-five country houses reported a loss of more than a thousand trees in their grounds.

Nothing perhaps sums up the extent and particular nature of the devastation in London better than the fact that on the day after the Great Storm the price of tiles rocketed from 21s. to 120s. a thousand.

In the evening of Friday, 26 November the Eddystone showed a light as usual. Its yellow glare was visible until shortly before midnight. By daybreak on Saturday there was no sign that the lighthouse had ever existed, except for a few warped and broken stumps of iron which, sprouting from the red rock like distraught fingers, seemed to be groping helplessly for the tower that they had failed to hold.

Henry Winstanley's wish had been mercilessly granted. He had been in his lighthouse 'during the greatest storm that ever was'.

CHAPTER SEVEN

Wonders and Waterworkes

POSTERITY has not been kind to Winstanley. Sentimentalists have falsely romanticized him, students of lighthouse history and practice have ridiculed him. The former include a number of people who felt impelled to commemorate their regard for him in verse.

An anonymous early Victorian produced an epic poem many pages long, of which the following is an extract:

> And first in fame great Winstanley appears!
> The noblest architect of ancient years;
> Though long destroyed by the resistless storm,—
> His ardent genius doth my bosom warm.
> Where tempest reign'd he boldly took his stand,
> And, delug'd o'er, the mighty works command;
> An hundred feet the wond'rous structure rose,
> And darts its beams, the guide of friends and foes . . .

The Victorian poet, Jean Ingelow, recorded her homage in a ballad of seventy-five verses which begins:

> Winstanley's deed, you kindly folk,
>   With it I fill my lay,
> And a nobler man ne'er walk'd the world,
>   Let his name be what it may.

And ends:

> Many fair tombs in the glorious glooms,
>   At Westminster they show;
> The brave and the great lie there in state:—
>   Winstanley lieth low.

There is this at least to be said for these effusions, typical of many: they indicate the impact of the Winstanley story, even a century and a half after his death, and it is significant in this connection that later references to the Great Storm of 1703 invariably described it as 'the storm in which the first Eddystone lighthouse was blown down with the builder inside it'.

Serious commentators have been inclined to go to the other extreme and dismiss Winstanley as a whimsical charlatan who had no business to be building lighthouses anyway. With monotonous regularity they contemptuously liken his structure to a Chinese pagoda. They are scathing about its ornamentation, and imply that it was so unpractical that it deserved what it got.

Both the critics and the sentimentalists have failed to see Winstanley's achievement in perspective—the perspective of its age, of the technical facilities available to him, and of the character of the man himself. It is obvious that by modern standards the design of the building was unsuitable. But there was no precedent. Winstanley was doing something that had never been done before. No one had ever built a lighthouse on a small, sea-swept rock. There was at the time no means of scientifically measuring the force of the wind and the waves. There was no previous experience to guide the choice of materials or the method of their fixture. All Winstanley could do was to build the sturdiest tower possible on the limited area available and hope for the best. He was carrying out an act of faith. It was a supremely bold effort to undertake. It was a remarkable achievement to build the thing at all.

It *did* last five years. It would undoubtedly have lasted longer had it not been for the entirely exceptional severity of the storm that put it to its final test. The external elaboration obviously *was* misguided, but it was a reflection of the man himself, and anyway cannot be said to have been the main cause of the building's failure, which was much more fundamental. Winstanley was a product of the Restoration, a showman with an innate love of intricacy and decoration. This was a part of him and he could not escape from it. He must have known about the celebrated French lighthouse at Cordouan, with its royal apartments, chapel, and sumptuous interior decoration, and may even have visited it. To a man like Winstanley it would be natural to try to go one better. Because of the size of the rock, his own building had to be much smaller than the massive

French tower. But by heaven he would make up for it in splendour, his kind of splendour. He would have a State Room every bit as elegant as the royal apartment in the French lighthouse—a State Room fit to receive the King and Queen if the occasion arose, and the publicity-minded Winstanley no doubt took every opportunity to try to make it arise.

But more important than any of this is the inescapable fact that Winstanley had shown the way. The spectacular manner of his going was as much in character as everything else he did. Only the *greatest* storm had sufficed to overwhelm this lover of superlatives and his precious creation. The showman in him could scarcely have devised a more spectacular exit. In the last resort this gifted eccentric was a seventeenth-century Toad of Toad Hall who died, as he had lived, with a flourish, taking his latest and greatest enthusiasm with him.

It was not a bad way to go.

Though Winstanley's master-work died with him, his other projects continued to flourish for many years under the direction of his widow, who seems to have inherited much of his commercial shrewdness.

A new edition of his engraving of the lighthouse was prepared to meet the demand stimulated by the dramatic circumstances in which the subject had been destroyed. To the many notices and inscriptions which already adorned this print was now added another which must have greatly heightened its sales-appeal:

> The lighthouse, thus built, stood untill that dreadfull storm of the 27th November 1703 which destroyed both it and its ingenious projector Henry Winstanley, gent.
> Many delightfull curiosities of his invention several drawings and engravings of copper plates he has left which are preserved.
> This fatall piece which was his last work may serve for his monument the house being his tomb, the sea his grave.

Nine years after his death the following advertisement appeared in the *Post Boy*:

> The fam'd House of the late ingenious Mr. Winstanley is open'd and shewn for the Benefit of his Widow with all the Curiosities as

formerly: and is lately butifi'd and well furnish'd, and several New Additions made by her; and it is on the Coach Road to Cambridge, Newmarket, Bury, Norwich, Lynn and Yarmouth, and is shewn for 12d. each and to Livery men 6d. This is known by a Lanthorn on the top of it; and was built and contriv'd by the same Winstanley that made the famous Water Theatre at the Lower End of Piccadilly, near Hide Park, and are both in possession of his Widow.

The April issue of the *Guardian* in the following year had this:

The famous Water Theatre of the late ingenious Mr. Winstanley is now open'd, and shewn for the benefit of his widow every evening between 5 and 6 of the clock; there are the greatest curiosities in waterworks the like never performed by any; and several new additions will be shewn this evening that were never seen before. Box, 2s. 6d.; Pit, 2s.; First Gallery, 1s. 6d.; Upper Gallery, 6d. Conveniences for coaches to be out of the way. This is at the lower end of Piccadilly, towards Hide Park, and is known by a windmill on the top of it.

This appeared a month after the signing of the Treaty of Utrecht, which brought the wars with Louis XIV finally to an end. The whole country was in holiday mood, celebrating the Peace. In London, especially, all entertainments were enjoying a boom as the victory celebrations continued into the summer. This was alluded to in an advertisement for the Water Theatre which appeared in the *Spectator* and the *Guardian* in May:

At the request of several persons of quality that came on Thursday to the Mathematical Water Theatre of the late ingenious Mr. Winstanley, when the house was full that they could not come in, this present day between 5 and 6 o'clock will be given to the spectator as before: 6 sorts of wine and brandy, to drink the Queen's health, all coming out of the barrel, with bisket and spa water; and, as peace is enlarged, there will be added Claret, Pale Ale, Stout, and water playing out of the head of the barrel when it is in the pulley. The house will be particularly adorned this night with several new figures and machines, playing of water and fire mingling with water, and a flying dragon, casting out of his mouth at the same time a large stream of water with fire, and perfumes, and a prospect of the Coaches going to Hide Park in cascades of water.

HENRY WINSTANLEY

A self-portrait

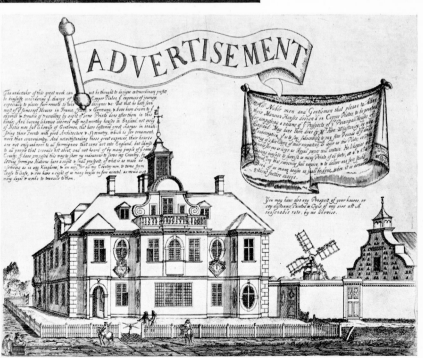

WINSTANLEY'S HOUSE AT LITTLEBURY, ESSEX

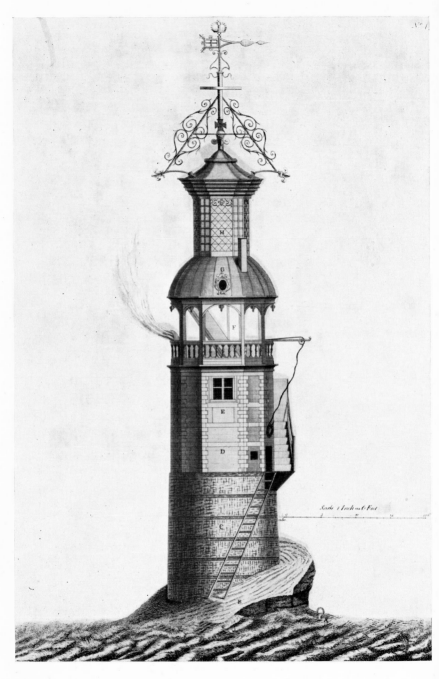

WINSTANLEY'S FIRST TOWER, 1698

Engraved by Henry Roberts, from a contemporary print,
drawn at the rock

It must have been quite a night, and it is evident that under Mrs. Winstanley's direction the Winstanley enterprises were by no means stagnating, and that she must have been making a comfortable income out of them. Nevertheless, she had slyly underwritten the notorious hazards of the entertainment business by petitioning the Queen for a pension on the grounds that the death of her husband had left her 'in very mean circumstances'.

Her first petition was submitted a year after his death:

Petition of Elizabeth, widow of Henry Winstanley, to the Queen. Her late husband for the great preservation of shipping expended in building the late lighthouse upon the rock called the Edystone near Plymouth about £5000 which was to have been repaid him with £50 a year for 50 years as a reward for his extraordinary service and invention thereof out of all such Shipping as received the benefit. About £2000 only was reimbursed him before the late dreadful storm of wind blew the same down when her husband lost his life: asking for the Royal Bounty.

Queen Anne referred the petition to the Lord High Treasurer who scribbled across it: 'Send this to Ye Trinity House to state Ye case with Ye opinion.' Trinity House apparently endorsed the claim, but no further action was taken, and in 1706 Mrs. Winstanley sent off another petition on the lines of the first but adding that:

the petition was recommended by the Corporation of Trinity House as a fit object of Her Majesty's charity and His Royal Highness [the Prince Consort who was also Lord High Admiral] to whom Her Majesty referred it, was of opinion that the Lighthouse was of very great advantage to navigation and that as her husband did very well deserve encouragement, so his widow being left in very mean circumstances was a fit object for her Majesty's charity.

A minute made on this new petition reads: 'Speak with some of the gentlemen of Trinity House.' The Brethren again supported the claim, and by a Royal Warrant of 1707 Mrs. Winstanley's persistence was rewarded by a grant of £200 from the Royal Bounty. A further Warrant gave her a pension of £100 per annum as from Lady Day of the following year. A

F

condition of the pension was that it would be payable only so long as Mrs. Winstanley remained a widow. It happened that some years later she fell in love with and married a French actor named Tessier. But the astute woman managed to keep the marriage secret, and continued to draw her pension. Henry Winstanley would have been proud of her.

Like every other town in the south of England, Plymouth suffered heavily during the Great Storm, yet when the damage was being reckoned up on the following day, the loss of the Eddystone lighthouse was the single item that dominated every thought, every conversation. For many people, especially seamen, there was a sense of profound shock in the idea that the building could have disappeared in a few hours of a single night. It was the more shocking because so many of them had watched Winstanley go out there that very morning. It was hard to believe that the Eddystone had just vanished.

Some of those who all along had been sceptical of the lighthouse's chance of survival could not resist saying that they were not surprised. They had known this must happen sooner or later. And some of them said it with a sneer. But the sneers soon froze on their faces.

Two nights after the storm the *Winchelsea*, a large merchantman homeward-bound from Virginia with a cargo of tobacco, entered the English Channel after one of the worst Atlantic crossings any of its crew could remember. It had been buffeted by gales from the time it left the American coast. Gale had followed gale, each one worse than the last. Then, two nights ago, as they were nearing the Western Approaches they had been hit by something the like of which even the oldest of them could not remember having experienced before. Most of them had doubted whether they would live through the night. Certainly no landsman would ever believe what they had gone through.

They had never been so pleased to see the Channel. Tomorrow they would ride into Plymouth Sound. Plymouth Sound was the most desirable stretch of water in the world, and they would certainly be glad to see it again. In the afternoon they sighted the Lizard, and driving steadily into the dusk

and then the darkness the Captain searched ahead for the Eddystone light. It would not be long now. They had a good breeze
behind them and were making good time. At any moment the
light should come into view.

Not only the Captain, but every other man on deck was
watching for the Eddystone light. They could not help doing.
In these last few years the first glimpse of the light had become
the great moment of every voyage. The Eddystone light meant
home. Every man on deck was peering into the darkness, straining to pick up the light. It could not be long now.

The Captain became anxious. They ought to have seen the
light by now. He was on course. He knew he was on course.
He knew how long it was since they had left the Lizard behind.
The Eddystone must be near. Had they forgotten to light
up that night? But that was impossible. It could not be fog,
there was no hint of any fog that night. Had he taken too wide
a course? Had he headed too much towards the centre of the
Channel? He peered desperately to port to see if he had taken
it too wide, and perhaps passed the Eddystone.

A look-out was the first to see the rocks and the flying spray
and then it was too late, the *Winchelsea* grated its way through
the western ledge, gashing both sides of its heavily laden belly,
then slewed round into the boiling waters between this ledge
and the central reef, and whichever way it turned or rolled in
its death agonies there were more teeth to stab and tear at its
flanks, and within a few minutes it had been broken. Two men
managed to get away in a boat. The rest died on a reef which
they knew could not possibly be the Eddystone because on the
Eddystone there was a lighthouse.

When the news reached Plymouth the effect was shattering.
For five years not a single ship had been lost on the Eddystone.
Now, within two days of the lighthouse being destroyed, a great
ship had been ground to bits on the reef. It was a terrifying
vindication of Winstanley's achievement. It was shocking and
frightening. They had grown used to the lighthouse. They had
grown used to the idea that there were no longer any wrecks
there. They took it for granted. They did not think about it
any more. Now this. Two nights, only two nights after the
lighthouse. For five years the Eddystone had been in chains.

Within two nights of regaining its liberty the monster had struck and killed.

There were no more post-mortems on Winstanley's design. No more academic arguments about the feasibility of building a new lighthouse. The *Winchelsea* abruptly ended all that. It was no longer a case of why or how, but how soon. This was an emergency. All that mattered now was how soon a new lighthouse could be built.

CHAPTER EIGHT

A New Approach

To men who owned ships or sailed in them—and this included the Navy—the building of a new Eddystone lighthouse was a matter of urgency. To the seafaring families of Devon and Cornwall it was more personal than that, it was a matter of life and death. Yet the melancholy truth is that two and a half years went by before a new building was put in hand.

Early in 1705, just over a year after the destruction of the Winstanley tower, the Eddystone lease was transferred by Trinity House from the original lease-holder, Walter Whitfeld, to Captain John Lovet for a period of ninety-nine years from the time a new light was in operation. The articles of agreement authorized Lovet to apply to Parliament in the name of Trinity House for permission to build a new lighthouse and collect dues on the same scale as before. In return, he and his successors were to pay Trinity House an annual rent of £100 for the period of the lease. Sixteen months later, in the spring of 1706, Queen Anne signed an Act of Parliament authorizing Lovet to proceed. In July of that year the work began.

The reasons for this delay are not clear—they might be clearer if so many Trinity House records had not been destroyed—but it is not too difficult to guess at some of the factors which may have influenced it.

First, it is clear that the Brethren were no keener than they had been on the previous occasion to tackle so risky an enterprise themselves. The fate of the first lighthouse and the financial loss incurred by its backers was bound to have a deterrent effect on others. It was one thing to agree loudly in public that a new lighthouse was essential, another to undertake the task of financing one.

Secondly, the transferring of the lease from Whitfeld to Lovet

doubtless involved protracted negotiations and lengthy correspondence between their respective solicitors. Whitfeld's
financial loss is not known, but it must have been considerable.
Winstanley, it will be recalled, had only got back £2,000 of the
£5,000 he had put up. The new deal presumably involved
some measure of compensation to Whitfeld, and the two parties
no doubt argued about this for some considerable time.

Once the matter had been referred to Parliament, further delay would be inevitable. The Government had a major war on
its hands. In 1704, nine months after the Eddystone disaster,
came Marlborough's great victory at Blenheim, followed two
years later by Ramillies. What was a matter of life and death in
Plymouth might seem a trivial local issue in Westminster, something that must wait and take its turn with other minor domestic
matters. What is puzzling, however, is why the matter had to go
to Parliament in the first place.

By this time Trinity House was festooned with every kind of
Charter, Patent, Warrant, Grant, and Act of Parliament. These
went back many reigns, and the most recent—the Patent of William and Mary only a dozen years before—had given the Corporation a perfectly clear authority to build a lighthouse on the
Eddystone or authorize others to do so. It is hard to understand why the whole Parliamentary rigmarole had to be gone
through yet again and red tape seems to be the only possible explanation. To those who believe that permits and licences and
other tyrannies of officialdom first reached Britain in the mid-
twentieth century, it may be some solace to learn that officialdom was apparently doing pretty well two hundred and fifty
years earlier.

When at last the new Act of Parliament had cleared the way,
Lovet announced the name of the man whom he had engaged
to build the second Eddystone lighthouse. For the second time
the choice had fallen on someone who was neither architect nor
professional engineer. His name was John Rudyerd, and he
was a silk merchant with a shop on Ludgate Hill in London.

Very little is known of John Rudyerd. He was born in Cornwall and passed the years of his childhood in circumstances of
extreme degradation and misery. He was one of a large
family described by a clergyman who knew them as 'a worth-

less set of ragged beggars, whom almost nobody would employ, on account of the badness of their characters'. The Rudyerds seem to have lived more like a gang than a family, with petty thieving as their principal occupation. The young son named John was the one white sheep of this black flock, and he was made to suffer accordingly. The family hated him for being different. He was kept short of food and clothing and had to endure constant ill-treatment by a brutish father and bullying brothers because he shrank from them and tried to avoid taking part in their squalid activities. At last he could stand it no longer and, running away to Plymouth, found employment as a domestic servant. He must have been a boy of striking personality, because his employer was soon treating him more as a son than a servant. He sent him to school—where he did very well—then started him off on a business career. Within a few years John Rudyerd had set up on his own account in London as a silk merchant.

These few known facts at least establish that he was a man of exceptional character, ability, and personality. The fact that he was engaged to build the new lighthouse, and the way he set about it, make it equally clear that he must have had interests and gifts beyond those strictly necessary to the marketing of silk. It was a period when men of substance were increasingly dabbling in scientific theory and experiment. Science was a gentlemanly pastime. The learned societies were the medium through which thoughtful and enquiring minds could exchange and develop their ideas. Theoretical development was mainly in the hands of these amateurs, and it is safe to assume that Rudyerd, self-made man and prosperous merchant, was one of them. The loss of the first lighthouse was a subject that must have greatly absorbed the scientifically inclined. From his design it is clear that Rudyerd had made an exhaustive study of the Eddystone problem in terms, both of his own creative ideas, and of the lessons to be learned from the failure of his predecessor. It may well have been his pet subject, and through the learned societies and influential friends, his Eddystone theories would eventually come to the notice of those concerned with finding an architect for the new lighthouse.

The conclusion that he was a gifted amateur with flair and

imagination but no practical experience is supported by the choice of his assistants. To supply the practical knowledge and experience he himself lacked, Rudyerd was given two hand-picked Master Shipwrights from the Navy Yard at Woolwich. Why shipwrights? Because the essence of his design was that he approached the building of a lighthouse, not in terms of building construction on land, but as a form of shipbuilding.

Winstanley had challenged the sea with the constructional materials and outlook of a landsman, and the sea had beaten him. Rudyerd was going to fight it with the only weapons that had ever beaten it—the craft, guile, and immemorial skills of the shipwright and the muscular, tensile vitality of seasoned timber.

In every essential feature Rudyerd's design differed so diametrically from Winstanley's, that it seemed almost as though his policy was to note what Winstanley had done and do the opposite. At the same time, in fairness to Winstanley, it must be remembered that he was working in the dark, trying something that had no precedent. Rudyerd had the great advantage of being able to draft his plans in the light of the earlier failure. In fairness to Rudyerd, on the other hand, it must be said that a comparison of the two plans makes it clear that he had a much sounder knowledge of basic engineering and scientific principles.

First, there was the material. To Winstanley, in his innocent exuberance, all that seemed necessary was to use the heaviest stone. He overlooked, or was unaware of, the law of displacement, whereby the largest slab of granite, if undermined by water pressure, can be tossed aside as readily as a cork.

To Rudyerd the situation called for other measures. Stone was fine for building churches and mansions. But you did not sail the seas in stone boats. To withstand the power of the sea, you needed timber. This was a golden age of shipbuilding. For generations the shipbuilders of England had been developing their hereditary skill in fashioning wood into vessels that from generation to generation were becoming bigger and stronger. Wood was the logical material to pit against the ocean. Its quality was proven: the craftsmen who were available to cut it to any required shape were men of the sea, men for whom every day's work was a specific challenge to the sea. The decision to use wood, then, was Rudyerd's first main departure from Winstanley.

Secondly, there was the design of the building. Winstanley had again acted innocently, thinking only in terms of mass. Erect the broadest stone tower possible on the rock-space and hope for the best. So long as its base is soundly secured to the rock, the weight of the tower will break the force of the waves.

Rudyerd saw the fallacy of this: the greater the mass, the greater must be the effect of the waves on it. The point surely was to reduce resistance to the sea, not increase it, but at the same time to incorporate as much weight as possible. What was needed was not the thickest possible tower, but one as slender as practicable. At the same time, to make it stable, the greatest possible weight must be concentrated in its lower portion, especially at the base. For this purpose it must not only be a slender tower, but it must taper towards the summit. But even then the base would almost certainly not be heavy enough. Once again Rudyerd turned his mind to shipbuilding. What did they do to ensure the stability and balance of ships? They loaded them with ballast. Ballast—that was it! He would weigh down his tapering wooden tower with ballast. More precisely, he would incorporate a considerable weight of stone within the solid base of his wooden tower.

For additional strength and stability he added another ship-building touch—a mast, buried in the 'ballast' at the base, and running up the centre to the summit of the tower to give it a flexible spinal column.

So much for basic design. The third main consideration was the finish and final refinement of the tower, with special reference to reducing to the absolute minimum the building's resistance to wind and sea pressures.

Winstanley had not given any serious thought to this. Otherwise he would not have built the upper half of his tower in the form of a polygon, for it was asking for trouble to offer the Atlantic ten flat sides to beat against from any point of the compass. Nor would he have festooned the finished building with all those decorative embellishments, every one of which added to the strain the building would have to endure in stormy weather.

Rudyerd, on the other hand, had a very sound instinctive grasp of aerodynamics, though this would not have been his word for it.

First, the tower must be slim and tapering, and secondly, it must be round throughout its entire length. It must also be smooth, and for this purpose he decided to encase it with a final skin of upright timbers treated exactly like the hull of a ship. So that the roundness and smoothness should be carried to its logical conclusion, no excrescences of any kind would be allowed to break it except where absolutely unavoidable.

There had to be an iron staircase on the outside from the rock to the entrance door, but it was the merest skeleton of iron. The hand-rail round the lantern gallery was the same—the minimum framework of slender iron-work necessary to fulfil its purpose. The lantern itself was plain and functional. In place of Winstanley's riot of roof-top *chinoiserie* Rudyerd's single concession to aesthetics was a metal ball two and a half feet in diameter. The windows were so arranged that when closed they fitted flush with the tower, and no part of them projected. Apart from the single outer staircase, therefore, the tower was entirely free of projections or cavities except for a narrow cornice or lip which projected from the lantern gallery. This was considered advisable as a protection against heavy seas, which, running up the tower, would otherwise have smashed against the lantern windows. This overhang was designed to divert them outwards.

In its simple functionalism the design was well ahead of the mood of its time. In its attempt to adapt to a static building the principles of shipbuilding it was ingenious and original. It remained to be seen whether it would succeed in practice. Work began at the beginning of July, 1706, a month or so after the cheering news of Ramillies, the second of Marlborough's great quartet of victories, had encouraged the nation to think that a turning-point of the war had been reached.

Much depended now on the ability of Mr. Smith and Mr. Norcutt, Master Shipwrights of Her Majesty's Naval Dockyard, Woolwich, to translate the silk merchant's plan into a reality of timber, braced with iron and stone.

CHAPTER NINE

Rudyerd's Tower

IT was now Rudyerd's turn to fret under the tantalizing
vagaries of Eddystone weather: to sit in Plymouth for days
on end waiting for midsummer storms to die down; to
make the laborious journey to the reef, only to have to turn
back because it was too rough to land; to lose a precious
hour at the rock because a vital tool or some building material
had been washed away; to be constantly drenched to the skin;
to discover that hoisting heavy materials from a bobbing boat
on to a wave-swept rock was too frequently a major operation in
itself; to think longingly of the hours that could be saved if only
it were possible to set up a forge on the reef and have a blacksmith working on the spot. But in that first working summer
methodical progress was made with the foundations of the new
lighthouse.

Rudyerd had grasped that the key to the whole enterprise
was to find a way of fastening the base of the tower to the rock
so that it was immovable, and he was prepared to go to infinite trouble. Winstanley's method of cementing the foundation stones around twelve irons sunk into the rock was the beginning of an idea, but it was obvious from what had happened
that it was not nearly enough. Apart from the fact that the
rusted remains found by Rudyerd indicated that Winstanley's
iron supports had not been adequately leaded in, it was still
unsatisfactory to rest the foundations on a slope. They must be
on the level. That was the first thing. So Rudyerd set his men
to work cutting the slope, on which the tower had to rest, into a
series of steps. They found this more difficult than they had
anticipated. When struck laterally, the laminae of the rock
tended to chip off in uneven and haphazard flakes. It proved
impossible to cut it into the seven smooth steps that Rudyerd had intended. He was forced to accept a rough-hewn

compromise and console himself with the thought that it was at least something to have these approximately horizontal surfaces on which to lay his foundation blocks.

Next, like Winstanley, Rudyerd made borings in the rock to receive iron branches. But there were thirty-six of them as against Winstanley's dozen, and they were much more precisely designed and executed. They were slots, rather than holes, and sunk to a depth of 16 inches. The particular thing about them was their shape—they were dovetailed. The width of each slot was a uniform $2\frac{1}{4}$ inches, but the length varied. At the top it was 7 inches. As it sank into the rock it narrowed gradually to 6 inches, then widened sharply to 8 inches at the bottom.

The iron branch that was to be fitted into this slot, and gripped by its dovetail, consisted of two irons side by side. The first, dovetailed on both sides, filled about half the slot, gripping the waist of the dovetailed slot with one of its own correspondingly shaped sides. The second iron, which was to key the first one in place, projected on one side, to fit the receding waist of the first iron, but receded on its other side, to fit the vacant side of the hole as it was driven into it. When both irons were in position they formed together a metal mass with a waist that exactly fitted the dovetailed sides of the rock encasing them. It would already be impossible to pull them out together. If the clearance between the irons and the sides of the slot and any space at the bottom of it were now filled with molten lead they would be welded into a single iron that would be inextricably merged with the rock.

It was not easy to make these slots in the rock. First a penetration had to be made with a pick. This was deepened with a jumper—the heavy chisel-ended drill which quarrymen still use to make holes to contain explosives—and swinging heavy mallets on the treacherous surfaces of the Eddystone was never a simple matter. Then a second hole was sunk alongside the first, and the rock between them was smashed with a pummel, and the two holes merged into a single larger opening. The slot had now to be deepened in the dovetailed shape required by Rudyerd. This needed special skill and precision, as well as patience, for the Eddystone gneiss did not yield lightly to any kind of boring against its grain, let alone fancy boring of this kind to specific measurements.

No fewer than thirty-six of these slots were demanded by Rudyerd on a circular surface approximately twenty feet in diameter. Inevitably no two slots came out exactly alike. The measurements that have been given are what subsequent observers found to be the approximate average. This meant every hole had to be carefully measured, every one of the iron branches tailor-made to fit the specific hole for which it was intended. The irons themselves, six feet in length, weighed anything up to a quarter of a ton. It was a marathon performance, both on the rock and in the Plymouth forge where the iron-work had to be carried out to these exact specifications.

Now came the task of fitting the irons into the holes. The great difficulty at Eddystone was keeping anything dry. The rusted remains of Winstanley's iron-work found by Rudyerd indicated that the earlier builder had failed to overcome the water problem. He had used irons with a club-shaped base. To fit these it had required holes of considerable diameter. There were signs that the irons had worked loose in their sockets, and this could have been explained by their having been leaded in when the holes were not dry. On the Eddystone a hole had only to be in existence a few seconds before it filled with water. Rudyerd's method of overcoming this was ingenious.

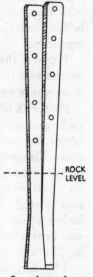

ROCK LEVEL

Iron branches keyed into rock.

As soon as the two irons comprising a single branch had been tested for size in their particular dovetailed hole, they were removed, every vestige of water was extracted from the hole, and it was immediately filled with boiling tallow which set hard. When the irons were to be fixed they were heated to a temperature of 550 degrees Fahrenheit and plunged in succession into the hole. The hot iron, scorching through the tallow, sent it streaming out of the hole, leaving only enough to seal up the clearance still left between the iron and its rock bed. This ensured continued water-proofing of the hole until the final stage of the operation was ready. Molten pewter was now passed up in a ladle and poured carefully into the hole, forcing out the remainder of the tallow and fusing rock and iron into an indivisible and permanent oneness.

Thirty-six times they went through this procedure, balancing precariously on the rocks, crouching to resist the wind, shielding their faces from the spray, and fervently hoping that the man with the ladle of molten metal did not stumble. By the time it was done Rudyerd could look with satisfaction on a twenty-foot circle of red rock, roughly hacked into steps, and bristling with thirty-six pairs of six-foot irons that were as firmly embedded as if they had been growing naturally out of the rock for centuries.

This was the first phase, to secure the irons to the rock. The second was to build the solid base of the tower and fasten it as immovably to the irons.

First, oak blocks were laid alongside the first step cut into the rock, and level with it. Then a set of shorter blocks was laid across the first blocks and the step, and level with the second step. The process was repeated, the timbers being alternately laid across and along the line of the steps, until the slope of the rock had been eliminated, and a level circular wooden platform now existed. The platform was solid except for a hole, eighteen inches square, cut through its centre and into the rock. This was to receive the mast which was to run up the centre of the lighthouse.

The thirty-six iron branches which Rudyerd had leaded into the rock were arranged in two concentric circles, except for two, which were planted astride the centre socket to grip the base of the mast. Each of the two irons of which every branch consisted had four one-inch holes at its upper end. As the base gradually came into being over the steps cut into the rock, and as timbers came into contact with the holes in the branches, they were bolted to them. But not with ordinary bolts. For extra security only jag-bolts were used, the jag or beard of this kind of bolt being a point something like a fish-hook and with a similarly tenacious effect. The number of branches allowed for nearly three hundred jag-bolts to be driven into the wooden base at various points. In addition, to secure these foundation timbers

even more closely, thick wooden nails were driven vertically
and laterally through pairs of blocks to bind them together.
The mast, which was set in position early in these proceedings,
was secured by jag-bolts to the two branches astride its socket.
Apart from any other consideration, the mast must have been
invaluable to the workmen as something to which equipment
could be fixed and materials roped, or simply to lean ladders
against.

Having secured his wooden base, Rudyerd went ahead with
the solid part of the tower, which was to continue for nine feet
above the foundation, and was to be a sort of layer-cake of
timber and granite. Each of the nine courses was one foot thick.
First came two timber courses; then five granite courses,
weighing 120 tons; then two more timber courses. Immense
care was taken to bind these courses into a single mass.

With the timber this was relatively simple. There was no
limit to the number of bolts and clamps that could be used to
bind adjacent blocks of wood together. With the granite it was
not so easy. The cement of the day was primitive, and at the
Eddystone it never had a chance to dry out. Many judges
thought that cement had been the main cause of Winstanley's
undoing.

Three things could be done about granite. It could be so
precisely cut and finished that the blocks would fit like a perfect jig-saw: but this was an ideal that could seldom be
realized. The more practicable steps to be taken were to have
the blocks drilled in advance with holes through which wooden
nails could be driven. These trenails, as they were called, could
be of any length and diameter required. Having been forced
through two adjacent blocks, they could then be tightened by
having splinters driven into them. Finally, the tops could be
sawn off so that the surface of the stone was left smooth. The
third way of binding blocks of stone was with iron clamps—
bars right-angled at each end, which were sunk into pre-
fabricated recesses in the stones to be joined.

But to make this possible an immense amount of care had to
be taken in advance. As each course was completed, it was laid
out on the floor of the work-yard in Plymouth to ensure that
every piece fitted. Where recesses had been made to take

clamps, the clamps were hand-made to fit them and, where necessary, modified until a perfect fit had been achieved. Not until the entire course had been assembled and submitted to the most minute examination in Plymouth were the individual blocks lettered and numbered (to facilitate re-assembly) and sent out to the Eddystone. It can easily be appreciated what delays could be caused if one or more of these tailored parts was lost through a high wave taking the workmen by surprise.

The other aid to solidity, meticulously observed throughout, was that adjacent blocks were always arranged so that no two joints overlapped. The jointing of the timbers making up the circumference of the wooden courses is also worth noting. For greater strength this was done in the style which carpenters call scarfing. The ends of the timbers to be joined were bevelled and notched so that they overlapped like hands extended palm to palm.

Finally, the layer-cake design made it possible for the wooden courses, between which layers of granite were sandwiched, to be clamped together with long vertical strips of iron. In this way the granite blocks were securely gripped together independently of the cement bindings between them.

This completed the solid part of the tower which was now nine feet above the highest point of the rock, nineteen above the lower. The entrance door was to be at this level, and from this point upwards Rudyerd continued the layer-cake procedure, but leaving a space for the door, and a central shaft six feet nine inches square for the staircase.

This semi-solid section raised the tower by another eighteen feet. First came five more granite courses weighing 86 tons: then two wooden courses followed by four more of granite, weighing 67 tons, and a final seven courses of wood. (The difference in weight between the first five granite courses and the second was due, of course, to the tapering of the building and the stairway shaft which cut through the second group of five.)

On a foundation immovably bolted to the rock, Rudyerd now had a 36-foot tower, weighted down by 273 tons of tightly packed granite as ballast, the bottom nine feet of the tower being solid. Now came the trump card—the encasing of this

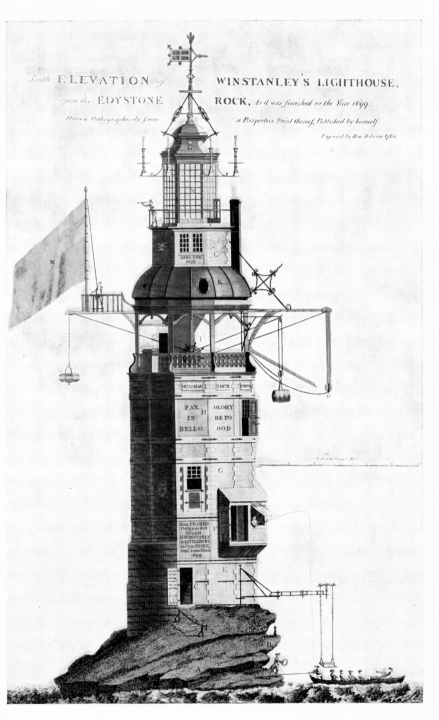

WINSTANLEY'S TOWER WHEN FINALLY COMPLETED
IN 1699

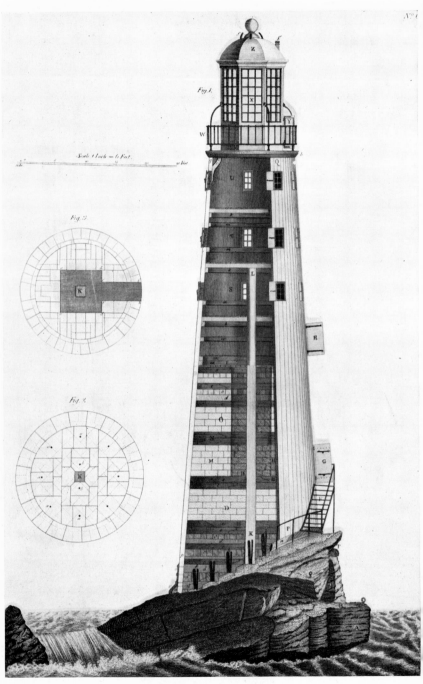

RUDYERD'S TOWER

Showing iron branches by which base was secured to rock, and central mast. The lighter sections are granite courses sandwiched between timber courses

tower in a skin of timber that would render it as impervious to
the assault of the sea as the hull of a ship.

The art of the early shipbuilders began in the forest. Long
before the craftsmen in the building yards had begun to cut and
shape the matured and seasoned beams, old men profoundly
wise in the subtleties of trees had combed the thick forests.
They had walked from tree to tree, studying them intently,
feeling them, sensing their secrets with an instinct that was in-
born and animal. These men knew infallibly when was the
right time to fell a tree and how long it must be allowed to
weather. The great oaks of Devonshire had no superior anywhere, and for more than two centuries English sailors had been
roaming the world in ships made from these trees. For the
master-stroke of his design, the timber skin that would make his
tower like a ship, Rudyerd needed the very best; only the
finest of the finest would do; this skin of oak had a heavy responsibility to bear. So the old men who knew and loved wood
as they knew and loved nothing else were set to work to pick out
the best of the winter-felled oak that had reached its final stage
of weathering in the Plymouth shipyards.

No fewer than seventy-one uprights would be necessary to
encase the tower vertically, and their preparation would call
for the highest degree of craftsmanship. At the base each upright would be one foot wide, nine inches thick. But as it rose
towards the summit the width and the thickness had to lessen
continuously, evenly, and uniformly. The whole point of the
casing was that it must be absolutely smooth. There must be no
vestige of a cavity or protrusion on which the persistent waves
could fasten. It was an assignment that only the finest shipwrights could approach.

The way they did it was to build up the uprights in deliberately varying lengths of between ten or twenty feet. The
reason for this was to ensure that the joints were scattered
irregularly about the surface of the tower and not adjacent to
one another, which would create areas of weakness. To ensure absolute smoothness of the joints themselves, the lengths of
which each upright was composed were scarfed to one another—
the method of joining, by overlapping their bevelled ends, to
which reference has been made. When the uprights reached

G

the top of the 36-foot solid and semi-solid tower, they were continued upwards for a further 34 feet to form the outer wall of four rooms, one above the other; the lowest a store-room, above it a living-room, above that a bedroom, and at the top a kitchen. The thick ceiling of the kitchen—on which the lantern would eventually be set—brought the final height of the tower to 71 feet. It was 22 feet 8 inches in diameter at the base, 14 feet 3 inches at the top.

As this outer skin of timber gradually took shape, it was treated in the same way as ships' timbers: the seams were caulked with oakum, and every square inch of wood was liberally coated with pitch. It remained only for the lantern to be set in position. But long before this was done Rudyerd had been able to improvise a temporary light, and amid much excitement at Plymouth, this was shown for the first time in 1708, just two years after the work had begun, though it took another year before the building was finally completed.

During most of this time four warships—*Roebuck*, *Charles Gally*, *Swallow Prize*, and *Albrow*—provided continuous protection for the working parties on the reef. This has misled a number of writers, including the normally reliable John Smeaton, into attributing the experience of being captured by a French privateer to Rudyerd rather than Winstanley, with the naval protection as its consequence. There is conclusive evidence, however, that it was Winstanley who suffered this interruption to his labours.

First, there is a letter from the Secretary of Trinity House to John Rudyerd dated 11 March, 1706—four months before he started work on his lighthouse. Although the letter to which it was a reply does not survive, it is a simple matter to surmise its contents. The Trinity House letter says that the Secretary 'thinks that the workmen need not fear being troubled, since the person that molested those formerly employed was severely punished by the French King, and the men sent back again'.

The inference is clear. Rudyerd would at this time be recruiting his workmen. Since it was only a few years since 'those formerly employed' (i.e. Winstanley and his men) had been 'molested', the incident would be fresh in memory, and a number of men were doubtless reluctant to sign on with Rudyerd in

case the same thing happened to them. His letter to Trinity
House obviously raised this point and asked for assurances
about adequate naval protection.

That Winstanley was the man carried off to France is established beyond doubt by the diarist Narcissus Luttrell. The
three pertinent entries covering a period of two weeks are these:

Tuesday 29 June 1697
A French privateer has seiz'd Mr. Winstanley ye Engineer, together with his workmen as they were erecting a Lightt House at
Eddystone Rock off Plymouth and carried him to France, destroy'd his work, but left his men behind them.

Saturday 3 July 1697
The Lords of ye Admiralty have sent to France to have Mr.
Winstanley ye Engineer (who was taken off Eddystone Rock near
Plymouth) exchanged according to ye cartel.

Tuesday 13 July 1697
Mr. Winstanley, ye Engineer, who was carried to France, is
come back, being exchanged according to ye cartel.

It was a measure of the close interest being taken in the new
lighthouse by the Navy—and possibly a sheepish recollection
of how the ship detailed to protect the earlier builder had
neglected its duty—that no chances were taken on the second
occasion.

Rudyerd had done what he had set out to do. He had built a
conical 'ship' and grafted it on to solid rock with sinews of
iron. It was ballasted with granite, presented a flexible tapering outline to the buffeting of the winds and the waves, and its
'hull' had been coated to resist the erosive ravages of sea-
water. Its design was first and foremost functional, and it was
severely without decoration of any kind. Because of this, and
because it was so true to itself, it had also a certain austere
beauty. The outer covering of upright timbers—their seams
showing up because of the pitch—gave a pleasing impression of
a fluted column. Especially when, in the wildness of its superb
marine setting, the lighthouse was first glimpsed through a faint
sea-mist in morning sunshine. And then, having completed the
work for which it seemed that he had been specifically born,
John Rudyerd vanished without trace.

Little enough is known of his earlier life, nothing whatever of what became of him after the lighthouse was finished. He just disappeared. He may have emigrated on the strength of his Eddystone success to continue building elsewhere, possibly in America. But the most likely explanation seems to be that he died. The malnutrition and extreme hardship of his childhood may have affected his general physical condition, and weeks of soakings and exposure on the Eddystone reef would exact a heavy price from anyone not in the best of health. There is one small clue which tends to support the theory of sudden death. A print of the new lighthouse was issued, drawn by B. Lens, engraved by J. Sturt, and purporting to be published by Rudyerd himself. This print, which includes a sectional drawing of the lighthouse giving actual dimensions and other statistical data, was shown by subsequent examinations of the building to be inaccurate in a number of major factual statements. It is hard to believe that Rudyerd, who approached the work itself with such meticulous practical care, would have passed for publication a representation of it with a number of glaring errors. It therefore seems fair to conclude that he died shortly after the print had been put in hand and that, without the editorial guidance of the builder, the artist had based his drawing on one of Rudyerd's earlier designs.

To this day, therefore, all that can be said with certainty of John Rudyerd is that he was born in a Cornish hovel, educated by a charitable employer, became a silk merchant in London, and happened to achieve immortality with a single work that had nothing to do with his proper trade. He was one of the great amateurs who are so much a part of the English historical tradition.

His lighthouse had been started in 1706 a month after Ramillies. It had shown a light for the first time two summers later, within a few days of Oudenarde. These were famous victories. Yet in terms of lasting human values, it could be said that the victory at Eddystone, which bridged the gap between the other two, was the greatest of the three. For it was a victory of skill and courage and imagination in an elemental war that never ceases. Marlborough had served his fellow countrymen, Rudyerd his fellow men.

CHAPTER TEN

Birth of a Tradition

RUDYERD had built well, and his lighthouse's behaviour
during its first few winters fully justified his design. It
required no attention other than routine running repairs, and now, when a particularly heavy storm hit the West
Country, Plymouth people no longer ran up to the Hoe with
telescopes to see if the Eddystone was still there. In 1714 Queen
Anne died, and was succeeded by George I. In the following
year the Eddystone changed hands. Captain Lovet died in that
year, and the lease was put up for sale by public auction. It
was bought by a syndicate of three men—Robert Weston,
Alfred Noyes, and a Dublin alderman named Cheetham—who
divided the property into eight shares, of which Weston and
Noyes each held three, Cheetham two. This was the only
occurrence of note during the first fourteen years of the
lighthouse's existence.

In 1723 a serious fault was detected. It was found that several
of the upright timbers forming the outer skin of the tower were
badly decayed at their lower ends. A form of wood-worm had
attacked them, penetrated to a depth of several inches, and
given the sea a chance to force its way between and inside them.
The proprietors appealed to the Navy for help, and the Navy
lent them the services of a foreman shipwright, John Holland,
from the Plymouth Dockyard. Holland carried out a major
overhaul of the base structure, replacing a number of the timbers with new ones, and for a time the trouble seemed to have
been cured. Then it started again, and Holland, though still
nominally on the strength of the Navy, was constantly being
borrowed to attend to the Eddystone. He made such a name
for himself as unofficial engineer in charge of Eddystone maintenance that when he was promoted and transferred to Woolwich as Assistant Builder there was consternation, and whenever

serious difficulties arose the Admiralty were invariably asked if he could be brought over to Plymouth to take charge. They generally obliged.

One such occasion was in 1734. The second of the Georges was now on the throne, Walpole was busy trying to keep the country out of a new continental war, and the Eddystone light-house, by this time twenty-five years old, was suffering from a particularly bad attack of its recurring wood-worm. John Holland, once more urgently summoned from Woolwich, tried a new way of tackling the problem. He covered the outside of a number of the uprights with copper plate, the inside with lead. In two other cases he tried a total encasement of copper. This was a method sometimes used to combat the same difficulty in ships' hulls. The theory was that the copper poisoned the pest. In the case of the lighthouse, however, the method did not work despite prolonged experiment, and worm-holes were actually found inside the copper casing.

There were various theories about this. Some thought that the copper on ships' hulls, being immersed continuously, de-veloped more toxic properties than it could do in a situation where it was only intermittently under water. Others said that it was nothing to do with poisoning the worm, but a matter of excluding it from the wood by the metal casing. This sealing, they said, could not have been properly carried out at the lighthouse.

The outcome was an acceptance of the fact that the en-croachments of the wood-worm and the consequent decay of the timber were something for which there could be no permanent solution. The owners would simply have to resign themselves to frequent inspection, maintenance, and replace-ment. To put this on a practical footing, Holland recom-mended to the proprietors a Plymouth foreman shipwright named Jessop to take general charge of Eddystone main-tenance. Holland himself could still be summoned with Ad-miralty permission in case of extreme emergency. By constant attention and frequent running repairs Jessop was able to keep the lighthouse in serviceable condition for another ten years. Then in 1744 (the year after Dettingen gave George II the right to appear in the history books as the last king of England

to command his army in battle) an exceptionally heavy gale
lashed the lighthouse from the east and ripped off portions of
thirty of its seventy-one uprights, so that it resembled a banana
peeled by shell-blast. It says much for the durability of Rudyerd's inner structure that it survived this stripping of its outer
covering; much for the skill of foreman shipwright Jessop that
he had the tower fully repaired in ten weeks, even though the
period of the work extended between late September and mid-
December when Eddystone weather is seldom charitable. He
had the benefit of John Holland's advice, but the main burden
of the work of restoration devolved upon Jessop himself.

The contribution of these two craftsmen, John Holland and
his protégé Josias Jessop, to the continued existence of the lighthouse was immense. It was one thing to build a tower in such
a situation, another to keep it there in serviceable condition,
and these two naval carpenters did this alone for forty-four
years. By experience they gradually built up and systematized a
tradition of lighthouse maintenance that set the pattern for the
future. It is an indication of the standards of craftsmanship and
responsibility expected of the skilled workmen of that time.

In the early summer Jessop would go out to the Rock, hear
the keepers' reports, and make his own inspection. During the
summer repairs would be carried out. In the autumn he would
make a final inspection before the weather broke, in case there
was some new damage requiring attention before the winter.
When John Holland died in 1752—by which time the Navy
had elevated him to the rank of King's Builder at the Deptford
yard—Jessop was more than qualified to take over completely
and see the lighthouse complete its first half century, an event
which now seemed a foregone conclusion, despite the attentions
of the wood-worm, and the green decay of the water-logged
lower timbers.

During these years there was coming into being a new folklore, the folklore of the keepers, the men who were willing to
endure this strange new life of solitude and confinement and
frequent terror in the middle of the ocean. To begin with they
were sent out in pairs, and their pay was £25 a year.

The work was not arduous. In the daytime there was little

to do but clean the lantern windows and prepare candles for the night. Between dusk and dawn they took it in turns to keep watches of four hours, when the main task was to attend to the candles. The work itself was simple enough, but this was more than made up for by the discomfort. The little round kitchen–living-room, the only room with a stove, was barely fourteen feet in diameter and eight feet high. Owing to the unreliability of the weather, no regular system of reliefs could be attempted. In winter they could be marooned there for weeks. In a gale the upper part of the tower rocked so violently that utensils were shaken off tables and shelves and the men were sometimes rocked out of their wooden bunks. The creaking of the great timbers added to the terror of gales, because so often it seemed that the tower must be on the point of breaking under the strain. The winter days and nights could seem desolately long on the Eddystone.

The effects of this cramped existence were not only physical. In summer the Plymouth boatmen did a considerable trade taking visitors out to see the Eddystone. The lighthouse was a national attraction and no one visited Devon and Cornwall without trying to fit in a trip to it. On one such occasion a rather hearty tourist who had been shown over the lighthouse remarked facetiously to one of the keepers that so far as he could make out they lived very comfortably in their agreeable state of retirement.

'Yes,' said the keeper, 'very comfortably if we could have the use of our tongues. But it is now a full month since my partner and I have spoke to each other.' Years later this story was quoted by Lord North in one of his speeches during the American War of Independence when, somewhat ponderously, he gave it as an example of 'how public service is liable to be obstructed by private dissentions'.

What is interesting is not so much the anecdote itself, but the fact that it should have become so widely quoted—an indication of the place the Eddystone had gained for itself in the national consciousness. It was already a national monument, and every story or scrap of information connected with it was greedily seized upon by a public that could not hear enough about this romantic and still not quite believable creation.

On one occasion a man who had been doing well as a cobbler decided to give up his trade and become a keeper. One of the boatmen who took him out to Eddystone for his first tour of duty questioned him about this. As a cobbler he was earning three shillings a day, what made him want to be a lighthouse keeper for ten shillings a week? The man said he had chosen to become a keeper because he could not stand *confinement*. This produced a loud laugh from the others in the boat. Defiantly the former cobbler explained that he meant *confinement to work*.

A less congenial occasion was reported when the lighthouse was some thirty years old. During a winter tour of duty one of the two keepers died. The other was afraid to dispose of the body in the obvious way—in the sea—in case he was subsequently accused of murdering his colleague. He therefore decided to keep the body in one of the lower rooms until he could attract the attention of a boat. He hoisted the flag, the recognized Eddystone distress signal, and hoped that it would not be long before someone came to the rescue. But the seas were rough, and continued rough without a break. It was a month before a boat succeeded in approaching the reef, by which time the corpse was barely capable of being moved at all. Despite the unpleasantness of his situation, this keeper maintained the light single-handed for the whole of this time. It was a tribute to his personal stamina as well as his devotion to duty. It also brought about an administrative change. The proprietors decided that in future there must always be three keepers on the Eddystone. It has been so ever since, and when other rock lighthouses came into existence they accepted four as the proper complement of keepers so that three would always be in residence, allowing for the fourth to be on shore leave. But it is to be feared that the proprietors' concern was less to provide a second witness that a dead keeper had not been murdered than to ensure continuous illumination.

So a new service grew, creating its tradition as it went along, developing its own mystery—for it was not quite like anything there had been before—and attracting to itself a special type of man who was drawn to it by the very factors that repelled the majority of his fellows: the loneliness, the curious eeriness of living with the birds in the middle of the sea, the isolation from the world, the reduction of living to basic simplicity, the necessity to live peaceably with two other men in cramped intimacy, the sharing of the deep primeval fear when the great Atlantic gales drove the seas about the tower which then seemed so infinitely frail.

For the many these considerations would always be daunting. But to a few men this was not so: reflective, philosophical, simple men—men who shrank from sociability and the multitude without perhaps quite knowing why—men who were self-contained and self-sufficient and deeply contented—men who sensed, even if they could not say so in words, the cleanness of nature—men, above all, who intuitively felt something god-like in the poetic mystery and the untamed grandeur of the sea: to such men this was a good life, an exclusive and secret life which was its own reward because it was dedicated to service.

A new breed of men was coming into being, and with them a new folklore. Their secrets would be passed from father to son, and in years to come their numbers would spread to every rocky coast in the world in the great international brotherhood of men who keep the lights, an exclusive race of sea-monks lighting the seas.

At Eddystone all this was beginning.

CHAPTER ELEVEN

A Night in December

THE summer of 1755 was like any other. As soon as the weather allowed, Josias Jessop sailed to the rock to make his annual inspection and take note of any faults the keepers had to report. As always, there were many repairs and replacements to be carried out after the winter scourging. This work proceeded methodically through the summer months. By 22 August it was finished, and the last of the work parties returned to Plymouth: the Eddystone was ready to face another winter. Between August and December the service boat made half a dozen journeys to the reef to land stores and make a routine check with the keepers that all was well. The last of these visits was on 1 December, when the keepers were able to report that everything was in good order: the only very minor damage that had been caused since the summer was that two bricks in the kitchen fireplace had been loosened in a recent storm. The lighthouse was as good as ever and well set to withstand its forty-sixth winter.

At midnight of that day, the unpopular middle watch until 4 a.m. was taken over by Henry Hall, the oldest of the three keepers, a man of ninety-four. He took post in the lantern, and the colleague whom he had relieved gratefully descended two floors to join the third keeper in the tiny round bedroom. Before him was the pleasant prospect of eight hours' sleep, for the third man, the one asleep, would be due to relieve Henry Hall at four o'clock.

It was blowing hard outside. The usual curtains of spray were rearing up against the three ledges of the reef seventy feet below, and between them there was the usual boil of white froth. At intervals a larger wave would smack the wooden tower venomously and make it shudder, and at other times a smoother wave would run up it like liquid flame. These climbing waves seemed to be deliberately trying to reach the lantern and extinguish it, but when they reached the top of the tower they would hit the bevelled cornice that had been placed there for this purpose, and spraying outwards just below the edge of the gallery, they would cascade prettily back on the rocks. There were not many such waves that night, but there were one or two for a period after high water. The scream of the wind was continuous, but on the Eddystone you got so used to this that you noticed it only when it dropped, which was very seldom. It was the same with the huge timbers of which the tower was constructed—you noticed only if they stopped their constant agonized groaning.

It was not what Henry Hall would call a really rough night but it was rough enough, and there was a fierce December chill in the air. He was glad to be inside the warm lantern for a short time. Not only were there the candles, but passing through the lantern and its cupola was the copper chimney from the coal-fire of the kitchen on the floor below. The hot, acrid smell of the coarse tallow could make the eyes and nostrils smart, but that was another thing you became used to, and it was better than freezing on the open gallery—at least for a few minutes.

Henry Hall went through some routine motions. He checked the number of new candles at hand. He snuffed one or two that were nearly burnt out and replaced them with new ones. He trimmed some of the wicks that were smoking. He made entries in the log. After a while he left the lantern and settled down in the kitchen. The candles were burning well. There was no need to stay in the lantern the whole time. After a time the burning tallow could become oppressive. It was more comfortable in the kitchen—and Henry Hall was ninety-four. The time passed slowly: in the middle watch it always did. From time to time he climbed up to the lantern to make sure that the candles were burning properly and then returned to the kitchen.

About two o'clock he shook himself out of a dose and slowly climbed the narrow stairway to the lantern gallery to make another of these inspection visits. As he climbed through to the gallery he was met by a billowing cloud of black smoke. The lantern was on fire.

On the open gallery there was a tub in which rain-water was collected. Seizing a leather bucket, Henry Hall began to fling water at the cupola on top of the lantern, where, after a few seconds, he could see that the fire was concentrated. At the same time he shouted as loudly as he could to rouse the other keepers. But men are not easily aroused at two o'clock in the morning. They were some distance below him. His voice had to compete with the noise of the wind and the sea. It was some time before he could attract their attention, and then they came stumbling up the stairway blinking and rubbing their eyes and not hurrying particularly, so that valuable time was lost. When at last they did appear he told them to get leather buckets from the store-room, and bring them up as quickly as possible, filled with sea-water.

During this time Henry Hall was doing his best to make some impression on the fire with the single bucket and the tub of rain-water on the gallery. It was a forlorn effort. The fire, he had soon discovered, had started in the cupola of the lantern. The copper chimney, it turned out afterwards, corroded where it passed through the cupola by sea-spray, had allowed a spark to escape into the inflammable crust of soot and tallow grease that, in the course of time, had accumulated inside the cupola above the candles. This meant that the old man had to throw the water several feet above his head to reach the cupola. It was a hopeless task.

Equally forlorn was the task of the other two who had to climb down and up the narrow stairway of the seventy-foot tower to produce buckets of sea-water. In spite of the discouraging difficulties, they did their best. While Henry Hall continued desperately to fling water upwards, the other keepers panted up and down the tower with buckets of sea-water. It was hopeless, of course, and the fire working steadily downwards had now gripped the whole of the lantern. But they kept at it until a new horror took them by surprise.

The cupola which formed the roof of the lantern was made of sheet lead supported on wooden struts, and by now the inferno inside the lantern was beginning to melt the lead above it, but for a time this was not apparent to Henry Hall on the gallery outside. When a man is looking upwards he subconsciously lets his mouth fall open. The mouth of Henry Hall, though he was not aware of it, was open as he summoned up the last of his waning strength to heave another despairing bucket of water at the top of the lantern. All of a sudden there was a terrifying crash, the cupola caved in, and a rain of molten lead came scorching down about the old man, searing his hair and face and arms, and then a shaft of cauterizing pain seemed to stab down through his throat and heart to his belly. He emitted a piercing scream and then, scarcely able to speak, began to moan that some of the lead had passed through his mouth.

The collapse of the lantern had set the wooden summit of the tower itself ablaze, and the best the men could now hope for was to shelter for as long as possible in the lower part of the lighthouse until the fire attracted the attention of boatmen who could come and rescue them. Painfully they edged their burnt and exhausted bodies down the stairway as the timbers at the top of the tower blazed with a crackling snarl that grew steadily in intensity as the fire nibbled its way downwards, and soon this roar drowned every other sound, including the scream of the wind.

If only the wind would move round to the south-west—its usual direction at this time of the year—there might be some chance of the waves putting out the fire before it had forced its way too far down the building. Only from the west and more particularly the south-west did the wind drive the sea up the long, shallow slopes of the west side of the reef, so that the waves piled up on themselves and swept up the full height of the tower. However hard it blew from the east—and it was blowing from the east now—the waves broke on the short vertical slopes on the eastern side of the reef, and though showers of spray would be directed upwards, the waves themselves did not run up the building. Spray was not enough tonight. Why, tonight of all nights, did the wind have to move round to the east?

The tower was now a great blazing torch, seventy feet tall, and there was a tragic irony in the fact that in its death agonies Rudyerd's lighthouse was lighting the sea, the function for which it had been born, more splendidly than it had ever done in its lifetime.

Floor by floor the outside timbers roasted until they cracked. Some caved inwards on to the thick wooden floors and stimulated the fire in its downward progress, others flew outwards, hissing directly into the sea or bouncing off the rocks in cascades of sparks. And every time a major section surrendered to the heat, a rain of red-hot bolts and iron clamps sprayed the floor below or the lower sides of the tower itself.

It was because of this constant rain of red-hot metal and blazing faggots that the men were afraid to abandon the building altogether and crouch on the rock. There was only one safe place on this rock the cleft—almost a cave—which cut into its north-east side, creating the ledge where they had the mooring-rings for boats. There was an overhang of rock at this point, and if they wedged themselves into the cleft they would have protection from the blazing pieces raining down from above. But there was one difficulty. This opening was submerged at high water, and the tide had not yet sufficiently receded to leave it exposed. They would have to wait. It was a grim wait. The fire was boring down on them slowly but steadily. They could not stay in the building much longer. Yet they must wait—just a little longer—until the water level had subsided another foot or two. If they tried to lodge on that precarious rock ledge too soon they would certainly be washed away.

Luckily, the lower the fire came, the thicker were the timbers which it had to consume. In addition to being heavily impregnated with pitch—which would cause them to smoulder rather than blaze—these lower timbers, thoroughly soaked already, were kept in this state by the sea. In consequence, the flames made slower progress as they moved downwards, and this gave the keepers a breathing space. Even so, the fire was uncomfortably close above their heads by the time the tide had finally left at their disposal this final sanctuary in the rock. To get there they had still to run the gauntlet of the hail of burning wood and metal streaming down from the dying building, but this was preferable to being roasted alive, and they were glad to make a dash for it down the outside stairway, and then crawl over the slippery rocks to the mooring-ledge where there was this precious cleft. There they were safe from the fire and could concentrate on resisting the efforts of the waves to wash them away. There were mooring-rings in this part of the rock and ropes attached to them. Provided that their strength did not give out, they could hang on to these until help came. So they braced themselves to endure an hour or two of being drenched and battered by the waves, and prayed that some boatmen had by this time seen the fire and reported it.

The first to see that the Eddystone was burning were some fishermen in Cawsand Bay just inside Plymouth Sound. It was about 6 a.m. They returned to the village of Cawsand and reported what they had seen to a local squire named Edwards. He immediately left his home and went down to the village to organize a rescue party, and in due course dispatched a fishing-boat and crew to take off any keepers who had survived the fire. This was evidently a more difficult task than it might seem, for it is recorded that as a result of his energetic exertions on that cold morning, Edwards caught pneumonia and died. In the absence of details it may be surmised that an elderly man, not in the best of health, left his bed hurriedly, flung on some clothes, rode several miles on horseback through an icy morning, and then had a difficult job to find men willing to undertake the journey—and that in the process he caught cold and perhaps strained his heart.

No Cornish or Devonshire boatman cared to sail anywhere near the Eddystone in winter. To take a boat there at all was regarded as a specialized skill which only a select few could accomplish. At any given time there were only one or two men who could do the Eddystone run. They were stars of their profession, and no one else particularly cared to emulate them. It was one thing to go out there and sail round the reef, another to attempt to tie up and land. It was not a particularly charitable age, and there would be no great rush to go out and attempt a hazardous rescue. It is likely that Edwards had a trying time mustering a crew, and this, coupled with the fact that he had in all probability left home without clothing himself adequately against a long, arduous, and infuriating battle with stubborn Cornishmen on a particularly freezing December morning, brought on the fatal illness. The records simply say that he was a wealthy man, noted for his generosity and kindness, and that the illness from which he died shortly afterwards was locally attributed to his experience that morning.

The fishing-boat eventually set off for the Eddystone, and in the meantime word reached Plymouth that the lighthouse was burning. Admiral West, who commanded a fleet then at anchor in Plymouth Sound, promptly ordered a sloop to make for the reef with fire-fighting equipment and a small boat which could go in close to tackle the fire and also take off survivors. Josias Jessop, the shipwright who had so effectively handled the running repairs of the lighthouse for so long, travelled in this ship. Alderman Tolcher, the agent who had for many years been collecting the Eddystone dues for the proprietors and had come to regard the lighthouse as the great love of his life, sailed from Plymouth independently with his son Joseph to find out the extent of the damage and discover what could be saved of the building.

The Cawsand fishing-boat was the first to arrive on the scene, but not until ten o'clock, by which time the fire had been burning for eight hours and was now eating into the solid nine feet which comprised the base of the tower. The problem was how to come close enough to take off the keepers. The wind was still blowing hard from the east, and blowing too hard for a boat to come alongside the landing-place.

The keepers were huddled together in the cave at the northeast point of the rock, just round the corner, as it were, from the course of the heavy ground swell sweeping up the west side of the reef. The east wind and the ground swell made a close approach by the Cawsand boatmen impossible.

After some delay they solved the difficulty in this way. First, they anchored the fishing-vessel as near to the reef as they dared. Then a party rowed in towards the rocks in the small boat they had brought along with them. As they did so they paid out behind them a rope attached to the larger boat. Finally, when they were close enough to the reef they threw a second line to the men on the rock and told them to loop it round their waists. When they had done this the burnt, exhausted keepers slithered into the icy, frothing waters to be hauled to the rowing-boat, which in turn was hauled back to

H

the anchored fishing-boat by the line that had been trailed behind the smaller boat for that purpose. With the three keepers aboard, the boat sailed for Plymouth.

Soon after this, Alderman Tolcher and his son reached the reef. Tolcher was determined to see for himself whether some of the tower could not be saved. He clung to a hope that the granite courses in the lower part of the tower would eventually defeat the fire. If the solid base could be saved it should be possible to rebuild the upper part fairly quickly. But it did not take him many moments to realize that there could be no question of this. The solid was well in the grip of the fire by now, and it was only a matter of time before the wooden courses which sandwiched the granite were burnt out, and then nothing could stop the heavy stone blocks tumbling down into the sea.

The dejected Tolcher remained at the reef long enough to watch a sporting effort by the Navy, which had now arrived on the scene. The sloop dispatched by Admiral West had sent a boat party in, complete with fire-engine, to see what could be done.

Bolder, but less cunning, than the Cornish fishermen, the sailors decided to attempt the impossible, a landing on the west side of the reef in the face of a heavy swell. When they were within a few yards of it a great wave rolled up behind them and, lifting the boat on to the rock, left it there, high and dry. But before they could take advantage of this piece of luck and unload the fire appliance, a second wave surged up over the rock and swept the boat back with it. Having survived these unnerving few seconds without damage to themselves or their boat, those in charge decided that it would be unwise to push this kind of luck too far. Nothing could be done to save the Eddystone now. It was too late. Like Winstanley's lighthouse, Rudyerd's would shortly be reduced to a few twisted irons in the rock face.

When the fishing-boat that had carried out the rescue reached Plymouth in the early afternoon a large crowd was there to meet it, to discover if the keepers had survived. As soon as they had been helped ashore, one of them, whose mind had been unhinged by what he had gone through, forced his way through the crowd and without a word to anybody made off through the town and was never seen or heard of again. The second of the two younger men was not too badly hurt. Attention was therefore focused on Henry Hall, who had had much the worst of it.

It seemed incredible that a man of ninety-four could have survived such an experience at all. After being badly burned he had had to spend hours on a wave-drenched rock in freezing cold. He could hardly speak, and when he did so it was only to mumble hoarsely that he had swallowed some boiling lead and if it was not removed he would die. He kept repeating this to everyone who came to see him; to Dr. Spry, who attended him daily; to the Eddystone shipwright Josias Jessop who visited him on most days; to his friends and his relatives. No one took much notice. He had been through a terrible ordeal. He was suffering from severe shock and burns and exposure. Obviously it must have affected his reason.

Dr. Spry was more sympathetic, but equally incredulous. Was it possible that a man of ninety-four, having swallowed hot lead, could survive a long winter night on the reef and at the end of it the further test of being dragged through the icy water at the end of a rope? Not to mention the discomfort of a tedious four-hour sail back to port? If there was really a piece of lead in his stomach could he have taken the medicines that Spry had been giving him? For five days his condition showed no sign of improving or deteriorating, but on the sixth day he seemed noticeably better and began to take more food, both liquids and solids. Surely a man with lead inside him could not have taken food and drink and medicine so readily—if at all?

On the twelfth day Henry Hall's condition suddenly worsened. He began to sweat feverishly, and painful convulsions gripped his body. Within a few hours he was dead.

A nagging curiosity now possessed Dr. Spry. Suppose, after all, the old man had been telling the truth. It still seemed impossible. And yet——? There was only one way to find out. The Doctor asked Henry Hall's friend Josias Jessop if he would witness an autopsy. Jessop declined, stating firmly that he would not be able to stand the sight of a body being opened. Two relatives of the dead man whom the Doctor approached were of the same mind, so he carried out the autopsy alone. And in the stomach of Henry Hall Dr. Spry found a flat, oval piece of lead weighing just over seven ounces.[1]

Beside himself with excitement, Spry prepared a full case history and sent it off to the Royal Society, only to receive the cold douche of scepticism which seems to be the traditional fate of the medical pioneer. In the absence of any independent witnesses, the members of the Society frankly refused to take the matter seriously.

This annoyed Dr. Spry, a young and ambitious man, and he determined to pursue the matter. He carried out a series of

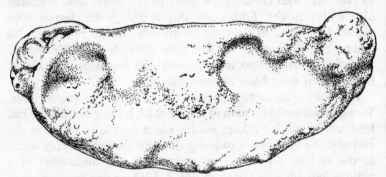

Drawing, actual size, of lead swallowed by Henry Hall.

experiments with live chickens and dogs, and now he always made certain that there were witnesses who could testify to his results. In the course of these experiments he found that these creatures nearly always survived the experience of having boiling lead poured down their throats, and were able to eat normally afterwards. One cockerel, which Spry served with three ounces of lead, was said to have tackled its grain more heartily after the event than before.

It is not clear just how the Doctor considered the cause of medical science was being advanced by these discoveries, and many people may think it just that they were brought to an end, not by the frosty disbelief of the Royal Society, but through the

[1] The actual piece of lead, which conforms to the shape of the pit of the stomach, can be seen at the Royal Scottish Museum, Edinburgh, which acquired it from the Royal Society of Edinburgh: an indication that Spry's report may have been received less sceptically across the border.

agitation of persons concerned about the animal cruelty involved.

This tragi-comic sequel, though something of a *cause célèbre* locally, did not distract attention from the harsh significance of the event itself. Once more the Eddystone reef was unleashed. What was to happen now? Was this rhythm of disaster to continue for ever? Must the days of an Eddystone lighthouse always be numbered? Was it to turn into a grim sweepstake to discover whose lighthouse could last longest, before succumbing in due course to a doom that was inescapable? Was there a curse on the place as men believed long ago?

In retrospect, Winstanley's early failure was understandable. But it did seem as though Rudyerd had found the answer. His sound design, his decision to use timber, and the fine craftsmanship of the naval builders and carpenters had produced a work of flexibility and toughness.

No one had foreseen that his tower carried within itself the seeds of its own destruction. For forty-six years it had defied the wind and the sea, the two forces it had been specifically designed to combat. It was a supreme stroke of irony that the timber which had seemed to be its triumphant strength was in the end the cause of its downfall.

Twice the Eddystone had defied attempts to curb it. The second time it could be said to have won on a foul. But it had won. To the craven-hearted it seemed that it would always win. Now, however, the reef was to meet a new opponent more considerable than those who had gone before, a man who would fight it with a mixture of pitiless engineering logic and inspired intuition.

The taming of the Eddystone was at hand.

CHAPTER TWELVE

A Man Named Smeaton

THE chief shareholder among the Eddystone proprietors at the time of the fire was Robert Weston, who with two others had bought the lease thirty-one years previously. In the course of time many of the shares had changed hands within the families concerned, either through death or marriage settlements. During this time the executive control of the lighthouse had been mainly left to Weston, and it was a stroke of fortune that the other shareholders were now more than willing to let him take full charge. The task of putting in hand a new lighthouse was to be much facilitated by the fact that it was largely left to one man, especially as he happened to be a man of considerable energy, drive, and—as it turned out—imagination.

Robert Weston behaved with exemplary swiftness. He wasted little time on post-mortems or recriminations. The lighthouse had gone. That was that. The important thing was to get on with a new one as quickly as possible. In the meantime there was an immediate duty to those whom the lighthouse had served. Within a fortnight he had inserted notices in the *London Gazette* and other newspapers advising all concerned that dues were suspended until a new lighthouse had been established, and that any shipowners who had been charged such dues since the fire would be repaid the money. At the same time he conceived the idea of mooring a floating light of some kind near the Eddystone reef to serve as a temporary measure until a new lighthouse had been built. He wrote to Trinity House asking for their advice about the practical aspects of this: the type of boat required, where it should be moored, and so on. Then he addressed himself to the problem of finding someone to build the new lighthouse.

Weston had made up his mind that only the best man procurable should build the new lighthouse. There had been two disasters within fifty years; the new tower had got to last; this was no time for compromise of any kind. Within reason expense would be no object. He simply wanted the best, and that meant a professional engineer who could bring a trained scientific and engineering mind to bear on the problem. The difficulty was how to find such a man. There was at this time no organized profession of civil engineering.

He decided to seek the advice of the only body of men who might be able to help, the Royal Society. They were, after all, the leading scientific body of the day, and if anyone could recommend a suitable builder of the new Eddystone they should be able to do so. Before doing this, however, he had to overcome the opposition of some of his colleagues. There was a school of thought which held that the Royal Society was no more than a collection of amateur theorists: that what was needed was the advice of more practical men. Weston nevertheless had his way and left for London to interview the President of the Society, the Earl of Macclesfield.

When he had heard what Weston wanted, Macclesfield replied without hesitation that there was a man named John Smeaton whom he could most strongly recommend. This Smeaton had first come to the notice of the Society seven years previously, when he was employed as an instrument-maker. His work in that field and some papers he had read to the Society had so impressed the members that they had elected him a Fellow at the youthful age of twenty-eight. That had been three years ago. Since then he had given up the instrument trade, which he had found insufficiently profitable, and gone into practice as an engineer. At the moment he was working in the north of England or Scotland. His friend Richard Wilson, the artist, would know exactly where he was and would no doubt be pleased to arrange an introduction. Macclesfield added that Smeaton was a man whom he had never known to 'undertake anything but what he completed to the satisfaction of those who employed him, and he [Weston] might rely upon it, when the business was stated to him, he would not undertake it unless he clearly saw himself capable of performing it'.

This fulsome testimonial, coming from so eminent a source, left Weston in little doubt that he had found his man, and delighted at having done so with such unexpectedly small trouble, he went straight from his interview with the Earl of Macclesfield to the artist, Richard Wilson, who promised to write on his behalf to Smeaton.

The circumstances of John Smeaton's birth and childhood were in marked contrast to those of his Eddystone predecessor John Rudyerd. He was born at Austhorpe Lodge near Leeds in 1724, the only son of a successful lawyer.

There was no indication at this time that Leeds would one day become a great commercial city. It was a small country town in a pleasant part of the green Yorkshire countryside, and the clothing trade that was to be the basis of its future industrialization was then so insignificant that it amounted to no more than a primitive cloth market conducted once a week in the open air. The clothiers would come in from the surrounding villages, carrying the cloth on their backs or on horses, and set up their stalls on the parapets of the narrow bridge in the centre of the town. Their traditional refreshment on these days was what they called a Brigend Shot—a bowl of porridge taken with a pot of ale, and followed by a twopenny slice of meat. After this innocent conclusion to the day's leisurely trading they would go home and Leeds would relapse into rural calm for another week.

Austhorpe Lodge was one of the grander mansions in the neighbouring countryside, and John Smeaton enjoyed there the agreeable life of a boy with well-to-do and rather doting parents. From the first he displayed an unusual talent for mechanics and constructional work of all kinds. The only toys for which he cared were tools with which he could make things, and he soon graduated from static models to ones that 'worked'. He was never so happy as when there were workmen in the house—especially carpenters and joiners—and would watch them for hours on end, questioning them closely about what they were doing, and persuading them to show him how to use tools. He would then go off and try to do what he had seen them doing.

He once spent a morning watching a party of millwrights at work. That afternoon he was found on the roof of one of his father's barns trying to construct a windmill. On another occasion he found workmen fixing a pump, and before leaving them wheedled some sections of piping out of them. Taking them home with him, he succeeded in constructing a working water-pump of his own.

For the main part of his education he was sent to the local Grammar School, and during his time there this pattern of development became more marked. He was brilliant at mathematics, but below average at everything else. He showed little interest in sport or games or any other normal boyish activities. His one idea was to escape as soon as possible to his workroom at home and make things. To the end of his schooldays he remained shy and awkwardly tongue-tied when with other boys; so much so that they nicknamed him 'Fooly' Smeaton, believing him to be stupid as well as anti-social. Yet in the presence of craftsmen of any kind this shyness deserted him. With complete self-assurance he would shoot question after question at them, pressing them to part with the secrets of their skills, and surprising them with the shrewdness of his observation and grasp. It was during his time at the Grammar School that Smeaton one day came upon a group of workmen erecting a steam-engine designed to pump water from a coal-mine not far from where he lived. It was an elaborate plant, and the boy made daily visits to the scene, studying every stage of the construction. When it was finished he built himself a miniature replica at home, and tested it on one of his father's favourite fish-ponds. It worked so well that the pond was quickly pumped dry.

His father was not pleased about losing the fish, but on this as on other occasions he showed himself to be a model of parental indulgence. He fixed the boy up with a workshop. Before he was fifteen Smeaton had constructed a lathe on which he could turn wood, metal, and ivory with considerable skill. He also taught himself to forge iron and steel. But Smeaton Senior still cherished the hope that his only son would eventually take over his legal practice, and with this in view he took him away from school when he was sixteen and put him to work in his office.

John Smeaton conscientiously tried to work up an interest in the Law, but without success, and it became increasingly clear to his father that he lived only for the moment of every working-day when he could escape from the office and return to his workshop, where he would often remain until the early hours of the morning. After eighteen months of this his father tried a new plan: he decided to separate the boy from his workshop for a while. He sent him to London to continue his studies there. The distractions of London, he hoped, might help to cure him of his mechanical obsession. But London was no more successful than Leeds in arousing a passion for legal training. Smeaton put up with it for a few months, then wrote his father a frank letter in which he pointed out that he was interested only in engineering, that he wanted to devote his life to it, and seeking permission to give up Law.

It says much for the tolerance of this parent that he not only agreed but also assured his son of the financial support which he knew would be necessary, at least for many years. It must be remembered that there was no engineering profession at this time. It was considered beneath the dignity of a gentleman to devote himself to this occupation except as a hobby. To become a practising engineer was to reduce his status to that of the artisan, and the financial reward was in keeping with this. It was not *done* for a gentleman to place himself on the same level as the millwrights, who were the nearest equivalent to the civil engineers of the day. At a time when the class structure was extremely rigid it must have been difficult for the father to see his only son take this step instead of following in his own professional footsteps, and it is a tribute to his understanding that he gave way with such good grace.

Smeaton at once found employment with an instrument-maker as a learner-assistant, and he rapidly became skilled in this work. At the same time his home background enabled him to gain access to the exclusive Royal Society, whose meetings he attended regularly. He was thus able to supplement the practical experience of his working hours with a grounding in more general scientific and engineering theory. By the time he was twenty-six he had set up his own instrument-making business and was now not only attending meetings of the Royal

Society but also reading papers to them. The first of these was an account of some improvements he had made (in collaboration with another man) in the marine compass.

For the time being he was specializing in marine and astronomical instruments. But two years later he was lecturing the Royal Society on an air-pump he had developed, and later that summer he was telling them about a new system of pulleys he had devised for ships' tackle whereby a man could easily lift a ton weight. Papers on widely varied subjects followed at regular intervals, and before his twenty-ninth birthday he had been elected a Fellow.

During this period he also found time to study French, partly because the most advanced scientific books of the day were either French or Italian, and partly because he contemplated making an extensive tour of the Low Countries to study their canal and land-reclamation systems. He eventually made this journey in 1754, and was fascinated by what he saw. What impressed him particularly were the dykes with which the Dutch had rescued so much land from the sea, and the harbour and dock installations of Amsterdam, which were much in advance of the primitive facilities still offered by the Port of London. He travelled all over Holland and Belgium, mainly in canal boats, but much of the time on foot, and this tour of close inspection was a turning point in his engineering education.

On his return he found himself no longer interested in making instruments. A wider vision had taken possession of him, the vision of the creative engineer. He had seen how backward his own country was in many respects. It cried out for development. He could help. This, after all, was where his duty lay. Engineering was in its infancy, but Smeaton, ahead of his time, was perhaps sensing intuitively the progress that would be made in the next hundred years. It was time to make a beginning.

There was war again between England and France, the Seven Years War in which the two countries were contesting the hegemony of India and Canada. And so while Clive in India and Wolfe in Canada pursued one kind of national vision, Smeaton the quiet Yorkshireman began to follow another, infinitely less glamorous but not less important: a vision that had to do with matters such as land drainage, harbour works, canals, coast erosion, and river improvement. It was to this type of work that he now turned (having closed down his instrument shop), and he was working on a project of this kind in Northumberland when the letter from his artist friend Wilson reached him early in January, 1756.

Wilson was not a diffuse letter writer. His note stated baldly that his friend had been chosen as a proper person to rebuild the Eddystone lighthouse. That was all. Smeaton, not for nothing a Yorkshireman, was not to be swept off his feet by so casual an approach. He had heard of the Eddystone fire, but without any details. He knew nothing about the place except what he could remember of a picture of it he had once seen. To the best of his recollection it had seemed to be built mainly of wood, but he guessed that it must have a hard core of stone underneath and that it was therefore unlikely to have been totally destroyed. He imagined that what was wanted was a new wooden upper portion. This kind of job was usually advertised, and there would be a number of people putting up schemes for consideration. At the moment he had offers of work that would keep him busy for months. Frankly, he did not fancy giving up this solid prospect to go to London and work out a scheme that would have to take its chance in competition with others, and then might not be accepted. 'Therefore', he wrote in his diary, 'I received the call without joy, or indeed much emotion of any kind.'

In his reply to Wilson he said that he presumed that he was being invited to go and prepare a plan in competition with other candidates. In that case he had engagements and prospects before him which he could not give up for so uncertain an alternative. But if, on the other hand, he was 'absolutely chosen to this business', he would consider it a great honour, would undertake to finish what he was doing within a month, and then give up everything else to tackle the Eddystone assignment. Would his friend please be more explicit?

Wilson's second letter was as brief as the first, but it told Smeaton all he needed to know. The lighthouse (he wrote) was a total loss. 'As Nathan said unto David, "Thou art the man."' Towards the end of February Smeaton arrived in London.

CHAPTER THIRTEEN

Dovetails and Tree-Trunks

AT thirty-one John Smeaton had turned his inquisitive and perceptive mind to a great many branches of mechanics and constructional engineering, but the building of wave-swept lighthouses in the open sea was not one of them. He had never been in the West Country. Eddystone was little more than a name to him. He knew nothing about the nature of the reef, or the weather conditions that had created around it a centuries-old legend of dread. His first meeting with Robert Weston was necessarily devoted, therefore, to a long basic briefing on Eddystone and all to do with it.

Weston brought with him plans, sketches, and models of the two earlier lighthouses, and the considerable fund of knowledge and experience gained during forty years as one of its proprietors. Weston talked, Smeaton listened. By the end of a meeting lasting several hours the engineer was in no sort of doubt about what he had let himself in for. But it was not in his Yorkshire nature to commit himself to opinions until he had weighed up all the considerations. He contented himself with just one leading question at this first interview.

He had noticed that Weston seemed to be taking it for granted that the new lighthouse would be modelled closely on the previous one. This bothered Smeaton. It was a principle of his that he expected to be given a free hand with anything he undertook. It was already in his mind that he would almost certainly want to use stone rather than timber. Without wishing to come right out and say so at this early stage of the proceedings, he felt he had better sound out Weston tactfully. He did so with an indirect question that indicates his shrewdness as a negotiator.

Suppose (he asked Weston casually) he did happen to think of an improvement that would enhance the stability and permanence of the new building, would the proprietors be willing to consider it, even though half the period of their lease had already expired, and the improvement might make the enterprise more expensive than a mere re-erection of Rudyerd's building? Weston's reply was emphatic. They would consider it a duty to posterity to support *any* improvement that would make the new lighthouse more durable. The question of the lease did not enter into it.

This told Smeaton precisely what he wanted to know. From the answer and the way it was given he now felt convinced that he was dealing with a man who not only had an open mind but also a sense of responsibility that extended beyond the immediate self-interest of himself and his partners. It will be remembered that Weston and others had taken over a ninety-nine-year lease dating from 1708. By the time the new lighthouse was completed the lease would have only forty-five years or so to run. Less scrupulous men might have been content to save money by commissioning a building designed simply to see out their own tenure—leaving their successors to take care of themselves.

This exchange set the seal on the mutual respect to which the two men had been cautiously feeling their way throughout the long meeting. It was the first warm handshake in what was to develop into a classic example of one of the most rare and felicitous of human collaborations—that between the creative artist and the sympathetic impresario who is prepared to give him a completely free hand and at the same time protect him like a baby from the irksome background problems of finance and administration.

Smeaton spent the next few days poring over the plans of the previous two lighthouses and found them tantalizingly unhelpful except in the broadest way. They gave him general information, but never specifically answered any of his questions. 'They afforded me just so much light as to enable me to discern the want of more information,' he said. In the meantime he had soon made up his mind that the new tower must be made of stone, and aware of the existing prejudice in favour of timber, he decided that he had better dispose of this fundamental issue at once. He wrote to Robert Weston requesting an interview with the proprietors to put to them a 'primary and leading question'.

At this meeting Smeaton came straight to the point. He wished to build the lighthouse of stone, which would not only be much more durable but also not subject to the danger of fire.

The proprietors unanimously agreed that stone had obvious advantages, provided that a satisfactory method of using it could be devised. But there were a number of objections. They pointed out that Rudyerd's wooden building had lasted for nearly half a century and had then been destroyed only through the accident of fire. In the eyes of the public it had been a success. If a new type of structure was built and it proved, for any reason, a failure, there would be a public outcry, and the proprietors would be blamed for experimenting instead of sticking to a tried formula.

Another objection was that the general opinion among men considered to be sound judges was that the main reason why Rudyerd's tower had lasted so long was the elasticity and flexibility of the timber. They recalled the well-known stories about how the lighthouse had rocked in severe gales—so badly that objects were flung off the shelves in the living-rooms. This showed, they said, the forces that it had to resist. If it had not been flexible enough to give way to them, it must have been destroyed long ago. A stone structure, being inflexible and unable to give way to the force of the sea, would be more likely to be struck down.

Smeaton countered this argument by insisting that the agitation of Rudyerd's building in storms was due not only to a lack of strength but, even more, to its lack of weight. The building he had in mind would be much stronger and much heavier. And if such a building, being made of stone, would not give way to the sea, the sea (he informed them blandly) must give way to the building.

This naturally led them to ask how he proposed to achieve this desirable end. Smeaton, always a man to deal with one thing at a time, was not to be drawn. He said that he had not asked for this early meeting to debate how a stone building could be constructed, nor to discuss details. All he wanted to do at this stage was to put to them a simple question:

. . . and that was, if I could convince their *own* understandings
that a building could be made with stone, not only so as to be
more durable, but even more safe from every accident that could
be foreseen, and not likely to be attended with a charge enor-
mously more large, whether they would prefer such a building to
the last, which they had experienced could be consumed by fire.

Because, if not (he added), there was no point in his wasting
a lot of time working out a method of carrying out a design that
in the end was going to be rejected. He was a persuasive talker,
and it was a good move to keep referring to the fire. The proprietors unanimously took up his challenge. If he could convince *them* in due course that there was a feasible method of
using stone, they would accept his design—subject of course to
their not being overruled by a superior authority—by which
they meant the Admiralty or the Corporation of Trinity House.

As there could be no question of a visit to the Eddystone rocks
before April, Smeaton now had three weeks in which to sort
out his theories and produce a design.

He made a new examination of Rudyerd's plan to see how
much of it was worth keeping. He decided that the accommodation and layout of the four rooms was satisfactory, and he
liked the idea of the steps cut into the slope of the rock to enable
the foundation stones to be laid on level surfaces. In these two
respects he would follow Rudyerd. Now there was the all-
important question of the shape of the tower.

Up to a point he approved of Rudyerd's choice in this respect, the frustum of a cone. It was along the right lines. The
tapering gave stability to the lower part of the tower and
lessened the wind-resistance above. But it did not go far
enough. The base, Smeaton considered, was not large enough.
This was why the tower had rocked in rough weather. The
new lighthouse must be broader in the base. But if he followed
Rudyerd's conical design, broadening of the base would result
in a proportionate enlargement of the rest of the building. This
would increase wind-resistance and so defeat the advantage
gained by the broader foundation.

Weight was the weapon with which he had to fight the
waves. Weight was what mattered. Now suppose the base
could be *enlarged* and the upper part of the tower made *even*

narrower? Suppose the sides of the tower, instead of converging conically in straight lines towards the summit, curved inwards from the base like a tree-trunk? This would have the effect of lowering the centre of gravity and concentrating more of the tower's weight on the broader base. At the same time the narrower upper portion would lessen wind-resistance still further. Finally, such a shape would use less material.

All of a sudden the analogy with a tree-trunk caught

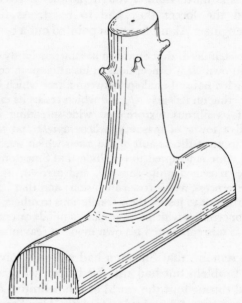

Drawing from Smeaton's engraving of his model.

Smeaton's fancy. An oak-tree, he mused, had to resist the same sort of violent pressures as a lighthouse. The trunk was broad at the base, and then curved inwards into a waist, after which the sides were roughly parallel until they swelled into branches. You seldom heard of an oak-tree being up-rooted. Another thing about a tree was the way in which the curve of its base reconciled itself with the often curving ground into which it was rooted. Delighted with this thought, Smeaton went straight to his work-bench and made a small model of a tree-trunk and fixed it to a curving piece of wood to illustrate

I

the manner in which a lighthouse might be fixed to an uneven
rock.

Broadly speaking, the analogy was a good one. It helped
Smeaton to crystallize his thoughts, which were in advance of
existing scientific definition. The little model of a tree was
going to be an invaluable aid when the time came to explain
to laymen what he had in mind. But in his enthusiasm
Smeaton pressed the analogy a little too far when he suggested
that there was more than a rough parallel between the two
objects and the forces they had to resist. As the Scottish
lighthouse engineer Alan Stevenson pointed out a century later:

> It is obvious, indeed, that Smeaton has unconsciously contrived to
> obscure his own clear conceptions in his attempt to connect them
> with a fancied natural analogy between a tree which is shaken by
> the *wind* acting on its *bushy top*, and which resists its enemy by the
> *strength* of its fibrous texture and wide-spreading ligamentous
> roots, and a tower of masonry, whose *weight* and *friction* alone
> enable it to meet the assault of the *waves* which wash around its
> base. . . . One is tempted to conclude that Smeaton had, in the
> first place, reasoned quite soundly, and arrived, by a perfectly
> legitimate process, at his true conclusion; and that it was only in
> the vain attempt to justify these conclusions to others, and convey
> to them conceptions which a large class of minds can never receive,
> that he has misrepresented his own mode of reasoning.

The fact remains that Smeaton had not only solved his own
immediate problem but had stumbled upon what was later to
be accepted throughout the world as the definitive design for a
wave-swept tower. A hundred years later Alan Stevenson gave
it formal definition:

> As the ultimate stability of a sea-tower, viewed as a monolithic
> mass, depends on the lowness of its centre of gravity, the general
> notion of its form is that of a cone; but, as the forces to which its
> several horizontal sections are opposed decrease towards its top
> in a rapid ratio, the solid should be generated by the revolution of
> some curve line convex to the axis of the tower, and gradually
> approaching to parallelism with it.

In the circumstances is it over-indulgent to claim for
Smeaton's oak-tree a tiny place at the back of the hall of

fame that contains the bath of Archimedes, the kettle of James Watt, and Newton's apple?

Having solved with this design the problem of weight, Smeaton turned to the other fundamental consideration, strength. How were blocks of stone weighing between one and three tons to be fastened to the rock and to each other so firmly that the finished building would be as cohesive as a monolith carved out of a single piece of stone? Nothing less than this standard would do.

Because of the situation in which the tower had to be built, cement could provide only part of the answer. There were no quick-setting cements in 1756. On the rock the cement would constantly be soaked by the sea, and it would be days before it set hard. Much of it would be washed away, and constant replenishment would be necessary. If he were to rely on cement alone, the newly placed stones would be endlessly disturbed, if not washed away, within a few minutes of being laid. To build in these circumstances would, as Smeaton pointed out, be as rewarding as rolling the stone of Sisyphus.

What it boiled down to was that he had to find alternative means of fixing the stones so that they remained totally immovable during the period the cement was setting, which might take days or even weeks. The most that could be expected of cement was that it would eventually provide the final touch to a state of absolute cohesion that had already been achieved by other means.

Smeaton was walking in London one day turning this problem over in his mind when his attention was caught by something he had noticed many times before without particularly taking it in. This was the way in which the pavements of the London streets were fashioned. The general jig-saw of the footpath was held in position by kerbstones locked at each end to similar stones running cross-wise. The point was that these binding stones were dovetailed so as to lock into one another. Dovetails. Commonly used in carpentry but never in masonry. This, thought Smeaton, could be the first thing. If his stones were cut in the shape of dovetails they could interlock and provide the beginning of that cohesion that was the essence of his problem. Each stone would be gripped by the one next to it, and in the centre of each course there could be a large keystone, also dovetailed, to which the outer stones could finally be anchored.

He would do the same with the foundation. He would improve the steps cut into the rock by Rudyerd by shaping them to take dovetailed foundation stones.

He was aware that dovetailing was only a beginning. It would help to secure the stones against lateral movement, and this security might be made absolute by a number of additional aids which he would go into later. But however firmly he could secure his stone courses laterally, he knew enough about the laws of water displacement to be only too conscious of the fact that the sea could still, if it washed away the cement, bodily lift the entire course from its bed. He would have to find some way of securing every course to the one below it. This would not be too difficult. A number of ideas at once suggested themselves. These could be worked out in detail later. He would not bother the proprietors with too much detail yet. For the time being it would be enough to sell them the general idea of his design. He asked for another interview.

Smeaton brought to this meeting some rough sketches of his design and the little wooden model of an oak-tree. He described the shape of the new lighthouse and his reasons for choosing it. He made much of his analogy between the tree-trunk and the lighthouse and of course the model was a great success. With this simple visual aid he was able to make his points clearly without confusing his hearers with technicalities.

So much for the design. With regard to the actual building, he could assure them that he was now fully satisfied that he could solve the problem of binding the stones to their foundations and to each other. He had a number of ideas in mind, with the details of which he would not trouble them at this point. But they might like to know of one basic principle he proposed to use. Then he told them about the idea of the stones being dovetailed to one another. It was his trump card. They were so convinced by what they had heard that they wanted him to submit his plans to the Admiralty and Trinity House right away. It was the salesman who now had to restrain the customers' enthusiasm. He pointed out that this preliminary plan

was purely theoretical, a work of the imagination. He had yet
to visit the Eddystone reef. When he had done so he might
find that some of his ideas had to be considerably revised. They
would all look rather foolish, he suggested, if, after receiving
the blessing of the two higher authorities, they had later to go
back to them and report that the plan had now been changed.
The next step, since they had approved his outline plan, was for
him to visit the Eddystone as soon as possible and make a detailed survey.

This was agreed and the meeting broke up in a mood of
cordiality and high hope. Smeaton gathered up his sketches
and his little oak-tree, and left for his lodgings. The proprietors followed him out into the street, eager to examine the
dovetailed kerbstones they had seen so many times but had
never really noticed.

CHAPTER FOURTEEN

The Unapproachable Reef

SMEATON arrived in Plymouth for the first time on 27 March. He was a happy man. He was confident that his preliminary theories of design were sound; he knew that he had the confidence of his employers; it was good to be escaping for the time being from desk work and theories and to be getting on with the job. He was also an excited man. At last he was about to set eyes on the Eddystone rocks about which he had now heard so much from others. His only complaint on arrival was of the time wasted in travelling: owing to the bad state of the roads the two-hundred-mile journey from London had taken six days.

He lost no time in seeking out Josias Jessop, the shipwright who for many years had been in charge of the maintenance and running repairs of the previous lighthouse. Jessop knew more about the practical aspects of that building than any living man, and it had been suggested to Smeaton that he might consider him as a possible assistant.

To begin with, the rugged old Cornishman and the young engineer from Yorkshire weighed one another up a little warily. Both Yorkshire and Cornwall breed cautious men. Smeaton was pleased to find that Jessop, in addition to being a fine craftsman, was also a skilled draughtsman and modeller. This was going to be useful. He was a mine of information about Rudyerd's building, and could answer all the practical questions that Smeaton had been wanting to ask. For his part, Jessop was relieved to find before long that he was dealing with a practical man, not merely a theorist with fancy ideas.

When the ice had been broken and the two men were beginning to warm towards one another, Smeaton dropped his bombshell. It was probable, he said, that the new lighthouse would be built of stone. The old man was shocked. How, he wanted to know, would it be possible to fit the outside timbers to a stone tower? Smeaton explained gently that if the lighthouse were built entirely of stone there would be no need for any timber.

Jessop raised the standard objection with which Smeaton was now thoroughly familiar: the rocking of the previous tower and how it could not have survived had it not been for the flexibility of the timber. Smeaton then produced his rough sketches and explained the principles on which his design was based. Jessop was impressed but not convinced. Further questioning wrung from the old man the admission that the problem of wood-worm had never been solved; that the lower sections of Rudyerd's timbers had become increasingly rotten and porous as a result of constant immersion and the activities of the worm; that it had become increasingly difficult to repair and replace this woodwork, and towards the end the tower had developed a pronounced list in the direction of the downward slope of the rock. Smeaton was eventually able to convince him that if the fire had not struck first, natural forces would almost certainly have finished off the lighthouse before very long.

Meanwhile he was anxious to visit the Eddystone as soon as possible. The wind was blowing from the north-west, the direction supposed to be most favourable for a landing. Could they not go that very day? Jessop shook his head. It was blowing from the right quarter, but it was blowing too hard. It would be at least two or three days before the sea quietened down.

This was Smeaton's first experience of a disappointment which to this day confronts the Eddystone visitor, when, looking hopefully at a sea which does not seem unduly ruffled, he is told, 'No landing today. Probably no landing tomorrow. Perhaps the day after.' Containing his impatience, Smeaton took the opportunity to introduce himself to the Commissioner in charge of the King's Dockyard and others whose co-operation he would be needing in the months to come.

This first visit to Plymouth eventually prolonged itself through two months, in the course of which only ten trips could be made to the Eddystone. Much of the time was taken

up with routine preparations of the kind that precede any
building operation. But an account of this extended reconnaissance is worth giving because the bare facts of it provide
so clear an impression of the unique difficulties imposed by the
Eddystone, and the character and painstaking approach of the
man who was now preparing to conquer it.

It was not until his seventh day in Plymouth, 2 April, that
Smeaton could visit the rock for the first time. He sailed with
Jessop in the ten-ton boat that had for some years serviced the
Eddystone and was known as the *Eddystone Boat*. A moderate
east wind was blowing when they headed into the Sound, but
by the time they reached the reef over four hours later rough
seas were breaking over it and a landing was out of the question. It was disappointing. Smeaton had to console himself
with the thought that he had at least seen the place. They
circled the rocks once or twice. 'As the tide was at its low ebb',
he noted, 'I had a good view of the rock, and an early opportunity of correcting many errors that I had been led into by the
incorrectness of the several models and draughts which had
come into my hands.' It was a small reward for seven days'
waiting and nine hours' difficult sailing.

They had to wait another three days before the weather was
fit for a second visit, and this time they were able to land—but
they had to work hard for the privilege—the journey took six
hours. Smeaton was able to spend two and a quarter hours on
the rock. First he looked for traces of the previous two lighthouses. He identified the holes in which Winstanley's foundation irons had been fixed. From these he was able to trace out
the exact site of the tower, and after examining it closely came
to the conclusion that it had been swept away in one piece,
taking a slice of rock with it.

Most of the iron branches that Rudyerd had set in the rock
to support the foundations of the second lighthouse were still
there, but the only other traces of his building were the steps
he had cut into the slope of the rock to take the foundation
courses. Smeaton found these rougher and cruder than they
appeared in the print of the lighthouse that he had seen. They
were uneven and unfinished. The execution had not come up to
the intention, and he saw that he would have to do better

himself. Having made a general survey of the rock, Smeaton next made some practical tests to discover how workable it was.

He removed his three-cornered hat and well-cut London coat and rolled up the sleeves of his silk shirt. Then, taking up an ordinary pick, he chose at random a point on the rock surface and attacked it vigorously while the boatmen watched him with amusement. He found that he could sink a hollow at the rate of five cubic inches a minute. Next he tested it for boring. Substituting a jumper and mallet for the pick, he was able to drill a hole at the rate of one inch in five minutes. Finally, he tried out a method of boring larger holes or continuous grooves from two smaller ones. The idea was to drill two holes close together, then break down the rock between them. He found that this, too, was perfectly practicable. It was hard going, but the rock could be pierced.

This initial survey and the tests he had carried out left Smeaton satisfied that a stone building was at least practicable. A major anxiety had been disposed of and he was in high spirits on the return journey. The only thing that did worry him now was the hazardous business of getting to the rock at all. The landing-place would have to be improved, and he must hire a second boat. Now that he had seen for himself the danger of losing a boat any time an attempt was made to land on the reef, it seemed an obvious precaution to take a spare whenever possible. He told Jessop to arrange for the hire of a craft similar to the *Eddystone Boat* for future use.

Four days went by before the weather was suitable for a third visit to the rock, and at midnight on 9 April he again headed for the Eddystone. There was little wind to start with, and they had to use their oars to make any headway. But as they approached the mouth of the Sound the wind swung round to the south-west—so that they had to sail directly into it—and began to blow hard. They rowed hard against it for three hours, but made so little progress that in the end they had to give up and turn back, reaching Plymouth six hours after leaving it. Tired and frustrated, Smeaton, who had done his share of the rowing, realized that he must resign himself to more of this. The only thing to do was to go ahead with other arrangements and seize opportunities to visit the reef as and when they occurred. It was no use sitting about, staring at the sea, and fretting, as it was so easy to do in the circumstances. There was much to be done away from the rock. He had to find a work-yard. He had to consider what stone to use and locate quarries that could supply it. It was important to make a start on these other arrangements.

It was a good thing that he made this decision then, because six more days went by before the weather became calm enough for another trip to the Eddystone. The day after the abortive night sail Smeaton began to look for a work-yard. He knew what he wanted. The yard must have a level area at least fifty yards square. It must be on the water's edge and accessible not only to small boats but to the larger craft that would be bringing in heavy loads of stone by sea. It must have a wharf or quay, or a place where one could be built, and there would need to be a depth of eight or nine feet alongside it. It would have to be in a part of the harbour well sheltered from the wind and so placed that the small craft, which would be sailing regularly to and from the Eddystone, could get in and out without difficulty.

He inspected a dozen possible sites without finding one that fulfilled all these requirements. In the end he settled for a field on the edge of Mill Bay—then a mile from the town, now the site of Plymouth's mercantile docks. The water was shallower than he would have liked, but he was prepared to dredge a deep channel through the mud if this became necessary.

He next turned to the matter of stone. The kind he had in mind, both for quality and availability, was the outcrop granite found on the Devon and Cornish moors. In colour and patterning it resembles petrified plum pudding and it is known locally as moorstone. He visited a quarry near Plymouth to see what they had and how they worked it. He learned there that some of this granite is harder than the rest. The harder kind, which was what they had at this particular quarry, splits most regularly, but it is more difficult to fashion afterwards into special shapes. Having watched the quarrymen at work for some time, he concluded that the less hard variety would probably be more suitable for the dovetailed shapes he had in mind. Before he could visit any more quarries the weather changed, and on 14 April a fourth attempt was made to reach the elusive reef.

They left Plymouth between five and six o'clock in the morning, praying that the moderate east wind would remain moderate and easterly for the next few hours. Once again they were to be disappointed. Soon after they were clear of the Sound the wind veered to the south-east and freshened, and the boatmen said that a landing would be out of the question. But Smeaton was developing an opportunist Eddystone philosophy. He ordered them to keep going. Even if he could not land, he could put the journey to some use. In the first place he wanted to go as close as possible to the reef to study the effect on it of a choppy sea when the wind was blowing from the south-east. Secondly, it was an opportunity to sail on to the Cornish fishing village of Fowey.

They continued to within two hundred yards of the rocks, and Smeaton was able to see for the first time the great curtains of spray that cascade continuously over the reef's three crests when the waves drive from the east into their vertical sides. Then he told the boatmen to make for Fowey, which they reached in the early evening.

There were two reasons why he wished to go there. Fowey, which has a sheltered harbour, is eighteen miles to the north-west of Eddystone, the line Eddystone–Fowey being roughly at right-angles to the line Eddystone–Plymouth. Because of this, when the wind is wrong for an approach to one it is right for the other, and it was normal practice for boatmen returning from Eddystone to use Fowey as an alternative if the wind was unfavourable for Plymouth. Smeaton thought this a good opportunity to see how this worked out in terms of time. His other reason for wanting to visit Fowey was that he had heard that there were good supplies of moorstone in that area.

He spent the next day with the Treleven brothers, who worked a moorstone quarry at Lanlivery six miles from Fowey, and had supplied much of the stone for Westminster Bridge. The granite there was the less brittle kind, and Smeaton found that what he had been told about it was true: it did not split as evenly as the extra-hard variety, but it was easier to work. He preferred it to what he had seen near Plymouth, but there was a problem of transportation.

To reach the nearest point of the coast from which it could be shipped, the stone had to be taken three miles across country in primitive wagons hauled by teams of oxen and horses. A ton and a half was considered to be the maximum practicable load. Smeaton expected to be using stone blocks some of which would be as heavy as three tons. It was going to be a slow business. It looked as though he would have to order his supplies from more than one place. But it was a beginning to have found a granite that seemed right for his purpose. The following day he sailed back to Plymouth. He had left there early on Thursday morning and had arrived back on Saturday night, having been no nearer the Eddystone than two hundred yards. But the journey had not been wasted.

The sea was rough on Sunday and again on Monday, but Tuesday was clear and calm, and a fifth attempt was made to reach the Eddystone. They left early in the morning. There was very little breeze, but it was right ahead and they had to tack and row strenuously to make any progress. They continued in this way for the whole of the day, but by nightfall they were still four miles from the reef. Then the tide turned against them and they had the infuriating experience of seeing the Eddystone across four miles of smooth water without being able to get any nearer to it. They dropped anchor with the idea of riding out the rest of that tide and running in on the turn. But when, during the night, it began to pour with rain and a strong wind came in from the south-east, Smeaton decided to return to Plymouth. They had not gone very far before the wind swung round to the north-east so that, as on the outward journey, they had to sail directly into it—and now it was blowing very hard indeed, and it was several hours before they made Plymouth, having been out all day and most of the night.

This trip—the most miserable, time-wasting, and exhausting to date—helped Smeaton to an important decision. It convinced him that it would be disastrous if the ambitious project taking shape in his mind were dependent on regular movement between Plymouth and the Eddystone. In four weeks he had been able to spend precisely two and a quarter hours on the reef. Only five times had it been worth attempting the journey at all, and on only one of these occasions had he actually been able to land. His admiration for the tenacity of his predecessors was now considerable, and they must have been lucky with their weather. But they had used lighter materials and had not attempted to achieve the standards of precision that he had in mind. What was it going to be like when boats heavily laden with tons of carefully shaped blocks of masonry were trying to keep to some semblance of a delivery schedule? If the work was not to drag on for years there was only one possible solution: a floating workshop moored as close as practicable to the building site.

A suitable vessel must be fitted out to accommodate workmen and materials, and anchored near the reef so that advantage could quickly be taken of every half-hour of calm weather. This was a key decision, less obvious than it might seem in retrospect, for it was no simple matter to moor a boat permanently in those turbulent waters. He consulted Jessop who thought that a fifty-ton sloop would probably be the most suitable vessel for the purpose. Because of the rocks it would have to be equipped with heavy mooring chains instead of cables. The inside lining would have to be caulked as thoroughly as the outside planking, and even then, to overcome the inevitable seepage of water through this double skin, it would almost certainly need two pumps. Jessop thought that if it were sloop-rigged such a boat could ride comfortably and solidly for long periods and, at the same time, if occasionally driven off its moorings in a gale, it should be capable of reaching a port under sail. But the matter would need careful thought.

At this point Smeaton suddenly remembered that Robert Weston had talked of establishing a floating light near the reef as a temporary expedient until the new lighthouse was built. The proprietors had bought a vessel for this purpose, a type of broad-beamed herring-boat known as a buss, and it was being fitted out on the Thames for its new role of lightship. It occurred to Smeaton that two birds might be killed with one stone—and the proprietors saved considerable expense—if this craft, named the *Neptune Buss*, could perform the double role of floating work-

shop as well as floating light. He wrote off to London that night
asking Weston if this possibility could be considered.

Two more days of rough weather gave Smeaton a chance to
deal with a number of administrative matters and to consider
further the question of building materials. He had been thinking that it might be a good idea to use Portland stone as well as
granite, and he had a long talk about this with Commissioner
Rogers at the Naval Dockyard. Portland was the best English
building stone and though less hard was more workable than
granite. The King's Docks at Plymouth were lined with it,
and it was possible to get an idea of how it stood up to the
effects of sea-water. Smeaton soon made an important dis-
covery in this connection.

Commissioner Rogers showed him a block of stone recently
removed from the dockside. It was riddled with perforations
similar to worm-holes in wood. These holes were caused by a
tiny crustacean which bored its way into the stone and enlarged the hole as it penetrated deeper and grew in size. It
came as a surprise to Smeaton that a minute shellfish could do
this damage, but he noted that its ravages were confined to
stones below low-water mark and therefore constantly immersed. It appeared from this that it would be inadvisable to
use Portland, or any other calcareous stone, for the outside of
the lighthouse—especially for the lower outside parts—and
indeed it might be best not to use it at all on the outside,
though it could safely be used on the inside.

Not (he explained) that he had any doubt that a tower made
entirely of Portland stone would certainly outlast a timber
building,

> . . . but in contemplating the use and benefit of such a structure
> as this, my ideas of what its duration and continued existence
> ought to be, were not confined within the boundary of an age or
> two; but extended themselves to look towards a possible *perpetuity*:
> and though it did not absolutely appear from what I had seen
> and heard, that a Portland stone building placed upon the Eddy-
> stone rock would in fact be penetrated by this kind of shellfish,
> which seemed to be in a great measure confined to and under low-
> water mark . . . it is inadvisable to run the least risk . . . I con-
> cluded that to give it all possibility of safety and probability of

permanence, it would be advisable to make use of moorstone for the foundation, if not for the whole of the outside work; it being of a quality not found either liable to be impaired by the above means, or subject to any kind of decay whatever by the injury of weather or time.

This was the second major decision of that week-end.

CHAPTER FIFTEEN

Preparations Completed

THE next day, 21 April, was calm. A moderate north-west wind blew all day, and at midnight Smeaton sailed to the Eddystone for the sixth time. The north wind blew them gently to the rock, which they reached shortly after five in the morning. They made an easy landing before low water, and this gave Smeaton a full six hours on the rock before the approach of high tide forced a withdrawal.

He had brought with him a theodolite and other surveying instruments, including a definitor—an instrument he had learned about from an Italian scientific treatise and which (like most of his others) he had made himself before leaving London. The purpose of this survey was to take measurements that would enable him to construct a model of the rock, and to complete his theoretical planning on paper. It was a lengthy business. Smeaton was never satisfied with half-measures. The model, thirty-two feet in diameter, would have to reproduce every angle and fold of this complex plinth. Using instruments which he had made himself and the knowledge of mathematics that he had been developing from an early age, he methodically measured heights and angles and curves and transferred them to paper so that they could later be re-translated into a solid replica of the rock.

All this took a long time, and by midday, when high water made a temporary retreat from the rock advisable, he had not nearly finished. He returned to the larger boat anchored a little way off the reef and waited for the tide to ebb. Two hours later he returned to the rock, and the water was now so calm that he was able to remain there for the next seven hours, until nine in the evening. For the last hour he worked by candlelight. Then he returned to the *Eddystone Boat*, which was anchored for the night half a mile to the north of the reef.

By five the following morning he was back on the rock and continued his survey until eleven, when a ground swell forced him to return to the larger boat. He hoped to be able to return to the rock in the afternoon as he had done on the previous day, but the wind had now moved round to the south-west and was freshening. He stood by hopefully until 5 p.m., but the wind was increasing all the time, and he had to abandon the idea. The breeze became so strong that it drove them back to Plymouth in two hours, which was considered to be almost a record time for the fourteen miles.

While at the rock, Smeaton was able on the side to make some useful observations, for future reference, on the behaviour of the sea. He noticed that on a perfectly calm day, with the water for half a mile around seemingly as smooth as glass, a scarcely perceptible ground swell could send an unexpected wave billowing over the rock, even though its peak was at the time nine feet above water level.

Watching from the boat anchored half a mile from the reef, he noticed that at low tide a comparatively innocuous swell, breaking against the overhanging breast of the rock at its western end, sent breakers to a height of thirty or forty feet. Yet at high water a much more violent swell, meeting the upper slope of the same rock, swirled over it without breaking at all. He carefully memorized these effects, for when the time came to work on the rock each and every one of the sea's foibles would have a vital bearing on the day's progress, and to be able to anticipate these variations in turbulent effect would save time and even lives.

With the mass of mathematical data that he had brought back to Plymouth he could now get down to the detailed planning of his building, and the preparation of the replica of the rock that he proposed to put in hand. A further spell of bad weather lasting five days helped him to give this work his fullest attention. By this time there was the completest understanding between Jessop and himself. As Robert Weston had foreseen, Jessop was to be the ideal assistant, and as such he was now seldom far from Smeaton's side.

Five days later, on 28 April, a seventh trip to the Eddystone appeared possible, and to try to make sure of getting there

K

Smeaton sailed as far as Cawsand Bay, three miles out, and lay up for the night behind Rame Head with a view to catching the following morning's tide and at the same time giving the journey a flying start. A change of wind to the south-east once again prevented a landing, so Smeaton did what he had done the previous time this particular wind had thwarted him—he took advantage of it to sail to Falmouth, which, like Fowey, is to the north-west of Eddystone. The purpose of this was to inspect another quarry where moorstone was produced.

The presiding genius here was a Mr. Box, and Smeaton liked his moorstone the best of all that he had seen. Box was working on a gravestone at the time, and this seemed to be one of his specialities. Much impressed by his craftsmanship, Smeaton thought that he had stumbled on a real artist and began to explain to Box what he had in mind. Box's reaction was disappointing.

> Such however is the nature of man [wrote Smeaton] that he may be great in one branch of his profession and remain small in another: for on communicating the nature of my design to him, I quickly found that he considered the forming and erecting of a well-shaped tomb-stone of granite as the greatest of human per-formances. . . . He seemed therefore rather frightened than pleased when I explained the nature and form of the work I should be likely to need . . . for to the execution of it he formed numerous difficulties, and did not know what to ask, either for his stone, his work, or for the carriage down to Falmouth.

Smeaton had to wait another six days before another attempt to land—the eighth—could be made. He set off in the early morning of 4 May, but he was not more than half-way across the Sound before squalls and driving rain reduced the journey to yet another frustrating test of endurance. Tacking and hard rowing carried the wet and frozen party no farther than Rame Head, a bare three miles from their starting-point, and once more the engineer had to return to Plymouth with a whole day wasted and nothing to show for it but a miserable soaking and a state of physical exhaustion.

To add to the wretchedness of this failure (the sixth in eight attempts), Smeaton was worried about a piece of news that had been given to him just as he was setting off in the morning. Some days previously forty French prize ships had been brought into the harbour. They were heavily laden with fish that was now beginning to putrefy, and for the most obvious of reasons the Navy were being pressed hard by the townspeople to dispose of them. A decision had therefore been taken to tow them out to the neighbourhood of Eddystone and sink them.

Smeaton heard about this as he was actually embarking. He dare not cancel the journey—chances of reaching the Eddystone were far too precious to be thrown away. But as soon as he got back from this latest abortive sail he went straight to Commissioner Rogers and protested. It was going to be bad enough to have to erect a building that would withstand the hostility of the sea without reinforcing that enemy with 'a thousand battering rams'—for that (he told the Commissioner heatedly) was what these forty ships would become after they had been dashed to pieces on the reef by successive storms. The Commissioner promised to speak to the Admiral. Smeaton, taking no chances, also sent a strong letter to one of the proprietors asking him to take the matter up with the Admiralty. This proved to be unnecessary. The next day the Admiral in command at Plymouth assured him that the ships would be sunk far from Eddystone. This was one of the few occasions when the equable Smeaton seems really to have lost his temper.

Another week went by before a ninth landing attempt could be made, and the rock was safely reached in the early evening. But no sooner had Smeaton landed and begun to make more notes on the behaviour of his chief enemy, the sea, than Jessop and the boatmen began to urge a quick withdrawal. They were unhappy about the wind, which was blowing from north-north-west.

The House rock, as Smeaton called the rock on which it was proposed to build, was on the most westerly edge of the reef. The landing place was between it and the central ledge, only fifty feet away. This channel, which they called the Gut, could be entered only from the north, the southern exit being blocked by the rock known as the Sugar Loaf. If the wind veered very slightly to north the boat, now tied up in the Gut, would be trapped. The men wanted to get out of the jagged-sided Gut while the going was good.

Smeaton agreed. The Eddystone had played a new card, and now this was something else that would have to be taken into account. He considered the possibility of levelling the Sugar Loaf with gunpowder, but rejected this as being both difficult to carry out and anyway not a final solution, since the submerged base would still be highly dangerous. And yet he could not remain dependent on this single entrance to the Gut as it stood; the experience of that afternoon had made this abundantly clear.

On the way back he thought of a solution. He had noticed that the Navy made use of mooring buoys. Might it not be possible to place one of these buoys a hundred yards to the north of the House rock, and link it to the landing place by a strong cable? The boats carrying workmen and materials could then haul themselves into and out of the Gut as required, regardless of wind or tide, and spend the minimum of time at the landing place before returning to the mooring buoy, well clear of the rocks.

The boatmen were doubtful whether a strong enough cable could be found for the purpose, especially to stand the chafing against the rocks at the reef end. Smeaton thought this could be solved by using chain for the last stretch where the line came into contact with the rocks. Before they were back in Plymouth he had designed a special type of windlass with which he proposed to equip all boats that would in due course be required to ferry themselves between the mooring buoy and the rock.

Four days later, on 15 May, he made his tenth and final trip to the rock, and was able to spend three and a half hours on it, completing his notes and observations, and having a last look round. But the visit did not end without the Eddystone giving another sharp warning of its power to hit back.

As the boat edged its way out of the Gut, the efforts of six boatmen, all by this time Eddystone veterans, could not prevent its being dashed against the rocks and holed—not badly enough, luckily, to prevent a successful if somewhat shaky journey back.

Smeaton had been in Plymouth seven weeks, far longer than he had hoped would be necessary. In the whole of that period of April and May a visit to the Eddystone had been possible on only ten occasions, and only four times had landings actually been made. But as a result of living with his project in circumstances that so often seemed deliberately contrived to break his spirit in advance, he now knew a great deal about the Eddystone. He knew from personal experience the variations of malignancy with which the sea, the tides, the winds, and the great reef itself would oppose him. He had learned the hard way the appalling time and space factor at the heart of his undertaking. He could leave Plymouth, therefore, with some solid conclusions that could not have been arrived at except through the protracted trial, error, disappointments, mishaps, and frustrations of the long reconnaissance.

To defeat the winds and the tides a floating workshop and base for the workmen would be anchored four hundred yards from the reef, so that advantage could be taken of every scrap of good weather. A mooring buoy would be established a hundred yards from the House rock, so that its connecting cable would ensure regular ferrying.

The model of the House rock which he proposed to have constructed in Plymouth would make accurate prefabrication of the building practicable.

His visits to the different moorstone quarries—and the divers problems of craftsmanship and transportation which each raised—had convinced him that he must use all available sources, and in addition must cut down the amount of moorstone used to the minimum. To be hauled across land the blocks would need to be kept down to a weight not much exceeding a ton. In effect, he would give the lighthouse a crust of moorstone, but inside he would use a more workable stone that could be obtained in unlimited quantities from a source with immediate access to sea transport. Portland seemed likely to be the answer.

These basic considerations settled, there was only one more policy matter to be dealt with before leaving Plymouth. This was the question of labour. The essence of this problem was how to ensure that the maximum amount of work was carried out on the rock whenever possible, and to reduce to the minimum the delays caused by the weather. With this in mind, Smeaton devised for the consideration of the proprietors, a labour plan which even by modern standards must surely rank as a model of astuteness, enlightenment, and equity.

This was Smeaton's 'Plan for carrying on the works and Management of the Workmen'.

1. That the Eddystone service should by all reasonable inducements be rendered preferable to any other common employment.
2. That therefore (as a punishment) any one failing his duty should be immediately discharged.
3. That the workmen should be divided into two companies; one company to be out at the rock, the other to be employed in the workyard on shore.
4. That every Saturday, the weather permitting, these two companies to change places; but the out-company not to return home till the in-company is carried out to relieve them.
5. Every man to have certain fixed wages weekly; and the same whether out or in.
6. Every man to receive something per hour over and above the fixed wages, for every hour he works upon the rock.
7. Every out-man to take all opportunities of landing upon the rock to work, when the weather serves, whether night or day, Sundays or work-days.
8. The in-company not to work either nights or on Sundays, except in case of necessity, and then
9. All extra work on shore to be paid for in proportion to double the fixed wages for the like time.
10. The seamen to be also at constant weekly wages, with an addition of a fee certain and proportionable every tide's work upon the rock.
11. Each company to have a foreman constantly with them while working upon the rock; to be paid more than the common workmen, and in the same proportion.
12. The engineer and his deputy to go off alternately week for week; and each week to go off as often, and stay as long as weather will permit, or the service require.
13. In case of sickness, or necessary absence of either the engineer

    or deputy, the whole (if possible) to be taken care of by the other.

14. All persons to victual themselves, but a bowl of punch to be allowed each company on their return ashore.

15. The foremen, workmen and seamen, to be paid every time the respective companies return on shore.

16. All work tools to be provided and repaired at the charge of the proprietors, and to have a mark put upon each of them peculiar to the Eddystone.

17. Every person hurt or maimed in the out-service to receive his common wages while under the surgeon's hands; and the proprietors to pay the surgeon. This to be allowed on the certificate of the engineer, deputy or agent.

18. Any person desirous of quitting the service, to give a week's notice to the engineer or deputy.

19. The foreman on shore to take an account of everything received into or sent out of the workyard; as also of the day's works of the company with him; under the check of the engineer or his deputy when on shore.

20. All smith's and plumber's work to be seen weighed by the foreman, engineer, or deputy on shore; and all timber or wood work to be measured, and other materials taken account of by the same on receiving them.

21. The foreman afloat to take account of time and landings upon the rock, to be checked by the engineer or his deputy when afloat.

22. An account of all matters done on shore to be given in weekly to the agent or accountant; and of all things done afloat by the proper foreman at the time of landing.

The key to this plan was the idea of having duplicate interchangeable working groups, and it was based on the assumption that the out-company would live afloat in the vicinity of the reef during its turn of duty.

Smeaton posted these proposals to the proprietors before leaving Plymouth, as he intended to break his return journey to London at the island of Portland, where he had an appointment with Roper, manager of the stone quarries.

It took the engineer very little time to decide that Portland was the answer to the question of what stone to use inside the outer crust of moorstone. There were unlimited quantities of it, the quarrymen were expert and very fast workers, there was a sheltered pier from which the stone could readily be shipped, and Roper was able to reassure him that there would be no difficulty about cutting it to the exact shapes and measurements required if Smeaton sent him wooden moulds. In addition, he found the price of the stone considerably cheaper than he had expected.

The brief visit to Portland was an agreeable interlude after the exertions and difficulties of the previous weeks. His business was concluded quickly and successfully. He was fascinated by the geological uniqueness of the place, and he even had time to delve briefly into local folklore.

As always, he was particularly interested in the methods and tools of the workmen. The rough hewing was done with a kevel, a hammer the striking surface of which is hollowed out to give a sharp cutting edge for breaking into the stone. Smeaton had never seen this tool before, and he was much impressed by the ease with which the Portlanders swung kevels weighing twenty pounds or more 'as though they were toys'. He was also struck by the uniform hugeness of these men, and reckoned that in fifteen minutes they cut as much stone as an average quarryman would manage in an hour.

Where, he asked Roper, had he managed to find such a collection of strong men? Roper assured him that he had not had to seek them out. Every one of them had been born on the island, and most of them had been no farther from it than Weymouth. (Though Portland is to all intents and purposes an island, it is possible, even at high tide, to walk across to the mainland and adjacent Weymouth.)

The air of the island, said Smeaton, must be particularly good to breed such men. Roper agreed that the air was good, but added: 'If you knew how these men are produced, you would wonder the less; for all our marriages here are productive of children.'

His curiosity now thoroughly titillated, Smeaton demanded more details. Afterwards he recorded the conversation.

'Our people here,' said Roper, 'as they are bred to hard labour, are very early in a condition to marry and provide for a family; they intermarry with one another, very rarely going to the mainland to seek a wife; and it has been the custom of the island from time immemorial that they never marry till a woman is pregnant.'

'But pray,' said Smeaton, 'does not this subject you to a great number of bastards? Have not your Portlanders the same kind of fickleness in their attachments that Englishmen are subject to? And in consequence, does not this produce many inconveniences?'

'None at all,' said Roper, 'for previous to my arrival here, there was but one child, on record of the parish register, that had been born a bastard in the compass of a hundred and fifty years. The mode of courtship here is that a young woman never admits of the serious addresses of a young man but on supposition of a thorough probation. When she becomes with child, she tells her mother; the mother tells her father; her father tells the young man's father; and he tells his son that it is then proper to be married.'

Smeaton was not satisfied.

'But suppose, Mr. Roper, she does *not* prove to be with child, what happens then? Do they live together without marriage? Or if they therefore separate, is not this such an imputation upon her, as to prevent her getting another suitor?'

'The case is thus managed. If the woman does not prove with child after a competent time of courtship, they conclude they are not destined by Providence for each other; they therefore separate; and as it is an established maxim, which the Portland women observe with great strictness, never to admit a plurality of lovers at one time, their honour is no way tarnished. She just as soon, after the affair is declared to be broke off, gets another suitor as if she had been left a widow or that nothing had ever happened but that she had remained an immaculate virgin.'

But the Yorkshireman was persistent. What about the time masons were brought down from London to help prepare the stone for Westminster Bridge?

'Yes,' Roper admitted, 'the men were much struck and mightily pleased with the facility of the Portland ladies, and it was not long before several of the women proved with child. But the men being called upon to marry them, this part of the lesson they were uninstructed in. And on their refusal the

Portland women arose to stone them out of the island. In so much that those few who did not choose to take their sweethearts for better or for worse after so fair a trial were in reality obliged to decamp, and on this occasion some few bastards were born. But since then matters have gone on according to the ancient custom.'

CHAPTER SIXTEEN

First Working Season

Back in London Smeaton started work on a number of elaborate scale models that would clarify his ideas not only to the proprietors but to himself. It was one of his working principles that the design on paper must always be converted into solid form for closer study, and much of his most important revision was invariably carried out in the light of what the model revealed. For this reason his models had to be detailed and perfect, and he always insisted on building them himself. But this would take time, and with summer weather approaching, this might mean sacrificing precious days when it would be possible to work at the Eddystone. It was a relief to him, therefore, to find his unusually accommodating employers (led by Robert Weston) as generous in the matter of time as they had been over money. They had spared him the time-wasting task of working out detailed estimates of costs—offering him within reason *carte blanche*—and now they respected his desire not to start building until he had completed all his preparations in his own way.

> Had they been of the same temper and disposition of by far the greatest part of those who have employed me, both before and since, their language would have been, 'Get on, get on, for God's sake, get on! The public is in expectation, get us something speedily to show, by which we may gain credit with the public!' This however was not their tone . . .

It was not until the last week of July, therefore, that Smeaton was ready to move down to Plymouth, but when he did so it was with the fortifying knowledge that his designs, amplified and clarified in model form, now had the fullest approval of the proprietors, the Lords of the Admiralty, and Trinity House. In the meantime he had been corresponding almost daily with Jessop, who had been appointed his general assistant, and practical arrangements in Plymouth were well advanced by the time he arrived to complete them.

Jessop had organized the Mill Bay work-yard according to Smeaton's instructions. A clerk arrived from London to take charge of the accounting and general office work. New yawls, specially designed for their purpose by Jessop himself, had been built to augment Smeaton's Eddystone fleet. Workmen had been signed on.

The labour force finally decided upon consisted of two companies of twelve men, each under a foreman. Each company consisted initially of six masons and six tinners, as the brawny Cornish tin-miners were known. Since the decline of the tin industry these men, famous for their powerful physique and exceptional strength, were much in demand as general labourers whenever there was heavy work to be done.

A wage scale had been fixed that followed out Smeaton's outline plan to provide every incentive to the men to spend as long as possible at the rock. During their turn as out-company, masons were to receive 2s. 6d. a day (as against 1s. 8d. ashore), with a bonus of 9d. an hour for every hour spent on the rock; tinners 2s. a day (as against 1s. 6d. ashore), with a bonus of 8d. an hour. The two foremen, Richardson and Hill, would receive 5s. a day at sea (as against 3s. 6d.), with a rock bonus of 1s. an hour. The seamen were placed on a similar footing, being attached for this purpose to one company or the other and paid at comparable rates.

On 3 August, 1756, Smeaton sailed to the Eddystone and marked out the centre point of the foundation and the lines on which steps were to be cut in the slope of the rock to take the foundation courses. There was just time, after he had done so, for the foreman named Richardson to scratch into these markings with a sharp pick and render them indelible before the rising tide forced them to withdraw. The building of the third Eddystone lighthouse had begun.

The target for this first season's work was the cutting and shaping of the steps so that the dovetailed foundation courses could be set on them the following season. If the cutting was completed before work stopped for the winter Smeaton would be satisfied. It would not be easy. Rudyerd had had the same idea, but Smeaton had been able to examine them and had noted how rough and unfinished they were. His own standards of precision were more exacting. This rust-red gneiss was difficult rock to penetrate, and the steps had to be cut to exact measurements. Unfortunately you could not use gunpowder, because that way you could not have precision—and you would almost certainly do more harm than good by disturbing adjacent rock that you did not want disturbed. There could be no question of gunpowder.

With Winstanley it had been a case of twelve holes during the first summer. For Smeaton it was six steps in a sloping rock surface that would resist every effort to break its crust.

In due course Smeaton hoped to have a large boat permanently moored near the reef for use as a base for the out-company and a staging point where tools and materials could be kept in readiness for rapid transfer to the building site, but this had not yet been arranged. Months previously the proprietors had informed Trinity House that they wished to provide a temporary floating light near the Eddystone and had bought and converted for this purpose the eighty-ton herring boat, the *Neptune Buss*. After a tedious and interminable correspondence Trinity House, who at first had agreed to this proposition, suddenly informed Weston that they had decided to make other arrangements and provide a light vessel of their own to supply a temporary light while the new lighthouse was building.

This led to much ill-feeling (and eventually to a law action which Trinity House lost), but in the meantime the *Neptune Buss*—now anchored at Plymouth—was going begging, but no decision had yet been taken as to whether it should be handed over to Smeaton to use as his floating workshop. For the time being he had to make do with what he had.

The bedrock of his work plan was to find a means of keeping the out-company in the vicinity of the reef during its tour of duty. Until he had something better, therefore, he proposed to solve this problem by using a sloop which he had added to his collection. The sloop could anchor near the reef for several days at a time and house the out-company between shifts— the workmen using a yawl to travel between it and the rock. At the same time a shuttle service of smaller craft would ply night and day between Plymouth, the sloop, and the rock to replace blunted tools with sharpened ones, bring out provisions and men as required, and assist in the relief of one company by the other.

On 5 August, two days after Smeaton had marked the House rock for cutting, this plan went into operation. Richardson's company had been chosen for the first turn at the reef and was standing by in the sloop at the entrance to Plymouth Sound. Smeaton sailed out to them early in the morning, and the entire company landed on the rock in the afternoon. They were able to put in four hours' work this tide. The engineer, having expressed himself well satisfied with the progress made, spent the night with the men in the sloop, which was anchored near by.

From now on there would no longer be days and nights, light and darkness. For these men there would only be tides. Work could be done only when the tide, flooding or ebbing, was below a certain level. Every precious minute of every tide would therefore have to be snatched at greedily to make up for the times when the weather prevented any approach to the rock at all. The financial incentive was such that every man was as appreciative of this as Smeaton.

Before sunrise the following morning they were back on the rock, and that tide's work amounted to six hours. On the afternoon tide they managed another five hours, working till after dark by the light of torches burning pitch and tow. The weather was for once being helpful, and Richardson's company was back on the rock as soon as the following morning's tide permitted, but after they had been working for less than an hour they were surprised to see a boat approaching with the other working company, Hill's, on board. Their only measure of time now was the tide and they had forgotten that it was Saturday, the day on which it had been agreed that the first changeover should take place.

Tools were handed over, Richardson's men embarked for Plymouth, and Hill's company, going straight to work, carried on for another five hours. The weather remaining fine for another week, this company was able to maintain the pace set by the first. Between 5 August (when the first out-company had started working the rock) and 15 August the two groups managed to average five hours' work on every tide. Hill's men, having a whole week of this weather, came off best, having put in 64½ hours during the seven days. The amount of bonus pay they collected that week was a valuable boost to everyone's morale, the foreman drawing 63s. over and above his basic weekly wage of 35s. and the others doing proportionately well. Smeaton himself was much cheered to be able to report that a third of the season's work had been completed in this short time.

But it was too early for excessive rejoicing. Even in August Eddystone weather is unpredictable. Richardson's company, taking over at the end of Hill's successful week, ran into such stormy seas that in the whole of their week they worked on the rock for just two hours, and for most of the time the sloop was forced to take shelter in Cawsand Bay, eleven miles from Eddystone. The important thing, however, was that the system had been put into operation and it worked. The only uncertain factor was the weather, and this would always be so. Thus the last week of August and the first two weeks of September yielded a total of 177 hours' work on the rock, but the last half of September only 20 hours, and the whole of October 23½.

In spite of the weather, the work, closely supervised by Jessop and Smeaton, progressed well, and by the middle of November the steps were ready to receive the foundation stones the following summer. In the meantime the proprietors had handed over the *Neptune Buss* to Smeaton for his use as a depot ship, and with some difficulty he had succeeded in mooring it a quarter of a mile from the reef.

It was an appalling ship to navigate, and mooring it to its two forty-fathom chains, each weighing 2½ tons, had scared the seamen who were required to assist. But Smeaton's specialized knowledge of pulleys had enabled him to construct tackle especially for the purpose, and after the mooring had with difficulty been completed, the seamen were the first to applaud the skill with which a landsman had conducted a strictly nautical operation they had thought to be impossible. Once the vessel was in position, the regular relief of the working companies each Saturday was much eased.

Work on the rock having finished for the season, there

remained the final task of fixing a giant buoy to the moorings
and bringing the *Neptune Buss* into Plymouth for the winter. It
took the combined efforts of Hill's company, four seamen, Jessop,
and Smeaton himself to fix the great buoy, but in the afternoon
of Monday, 22 November, the task was completed, thanks once
again to Smeaton's expertise in the matter of hoisting tackle.
But as the wind was now blowing at gale strength from the
east, they decided to make for Fowey instead of Plymouth.

It had been stormy all day, with continuous driving rain, and
as soon as they were under way Smeaton went below to his
cabin, removed his wet clothes, and looked forward to a good
rest, as he had had two exceptionally strenuous days. He had
been dozing for some three hours when he was aroused by a
great commotion above, and running up on deck in his shirt
into the blinding storm, the only thing he could discern
through the darkness was the terrifying whiteness of breakers
immediately ahead. John Bowden, one of the seamen, yelled,
'For God's sake heave hard at this rope if you mean to save
your lives.' Smeaton immediately grabbed at the rope on
which Bowden himself was hauling, as well as managing the
helm, and shouted to others to do the same. Their combined
efforts and Bowden's helmsmanship slowly swung the nose of
the boat round so that it no longer faced the breakers; and
after taking the full force of the gale on its beam, so that its
gunwale was dipping into the water, it righted itself and
began to answer the helm, and they knew they were under way
and moving away from the rocks.

Then the jib was ripped into shreds and to save the mainsail
they had to lower it so that only half of its surface was exposed
to the wind. Their compass indicated that they were now
heading south and the wind had veered to east-south-east.
Unfortunately they had no idea of where they were. Some
thought that they were short of Fowey harbour, others that
they had overshot it and were running against the headland
by Dodman Point. While the seamen argued about this, Smeaton
—who was becoming quite a sailor *malgré soi*—suggested that
the best thing to do would be to heave-to where they were until
daylight showed them how near they were to land. Since they
could not know for certain how close they might be to a dan-

gerous coast, their greatest chance of survival lay in keeping to the open sea, where now they appeared to be.

His argument prevailed, and it was strengthened by the nature of their craft. The busses were a Dutch type of herring-boat, and the *Neptune Buss* was one of several specially built in connection with a project to create a herring industry on a national basis. The scheme having fallen through, a number of these ships had come on the market. When Robert Weston first conceived the idea of establishing a temporary lightship near the Eddystone, he was advised that this type of craft would lend itself to the purpose if certain modifications were carried out. Accordingly the buss had been adapted for a static role. The deck had been made flush fore and aft, and it was ballasted with heavy timber for extra buoyancy. But it was a hateful object to sail, and all who had anything to do with the craft loathed it. On its journeys from Plymouth to its moorings near the rock it gave endless trouble and more than once took several days to get there. Smeaton afterwards said that it had caused more trouble than any other single factor in his working design. But it *could* ride a rough sea almost indefinitely and it was practically unsinkable. This was its single virtue.

So for the rest of Monday night the *Neptune Buss* tossed about like a huge ungainly cork while eighteen shivering soaked men struggled to exercise some semblance of control over it—a try-ing task, since even when it was using only half the mainsail the gunwales constantly dipped below the water.

Daylight, when at last it came, brought no comfort. There was no land in sight, and their compass and the north-east wind made it clear that they were being driven steadily to-wards the Bay of Biscay. Now came a difficult decision. The yawl which they were towing (and which might be the means of saving their lives) had shipped a great deal of water during the night, and its weight made it impossible to manoeuvre the awkward buss. A little reluctantly they decided it must be cut adrift. Only without it could they attempt to 'wear' the buss and swing it round to the north-west in an effort to reach some westerly point of the coast. At noon they sighted land on their windward side and guessed it to be the Lizard. They were confirmed in this feeling by the appearance of more land

L

immediately ahead—which must be Land's End. But they could not beat the north-east wind, and by the time they had got near enough to identify Land's End it was far to their windward. They had been driven so far to the west that they realized now that without a change of wind there was no hope of hitting the English coast.

As the storm abated a little in the evening they decided to make one more effort to force their way eastwards against the wind, hoping that the tide might help them to reach a Cornish harbour. They had a spare foresail, a mizen, and a storm jib. Hoisting these, they once more set a course for the north-west, but by noon of the following day (Wednesday) they had still made no progress. They were as far west of Land's End as they had the previous day been west of the Lizard. They knew then that without a change of wind (which, though now less stormy, was still stubbornly north-easterly) the English coast was beyond their reach. So they dropped anchor and considered the possibilities.

There seemed to be three choices. To use this wind to get them across the Bay of Biscay to a port in France or Spain; to stay where they were until the wind changed; to try for a port in the Scilly Isles.

They checked stores and found that they had provisions for a week. These would not be enough for a crossing of Biscay, for if the wind happened to change when they were almost across, they would need to take advantage of it, and their food would certainly not last the double journey.

If they simply waited for a change of wind where they were they might find themselves in the same place a week later with all their food used up. An attempt to reach the Scillies seemed the least of the evils, and they decided to try it—though with considerable misgivings, as they had no charts; none of them had even been there; and the rocks which surrounded those islands were as notorious as Eddystone. To get there at all would be largely a matter of guesswork and instinct, and they were debating what initial course to set when they sighted a ship sailing directly at them from the east.

There was a war on, and this might be a French ship, but Smeaton noted that their anxiety and weariness were by this time so acute that even the possibility of being captured and taken to France seemed preferable to the prospect of remaining in their present predicament. A distress signal was made, and the ship turned out to be the *White Hart* on its way from Poole to Guinea. The *White Hart* was able to give them their course for the Scillies, and they decided to lie to until four o'clock the following morning, Thursday, hoping that, by timing their start then, they would be able to reach the islands in daylight; and so stand a better chance of avoiding the rocks, signalling their presence, and even attracting the attention of a pilot.

That evening the wind dropped, and by midnight it was calm. Between three and four on Thursday morning, as they were heaving in the anchor preparatory to departure, a gentle breeze sprang up from the north-north-west. The laborious business of heaving up forty fathoms of cable became a labour of love. Men smiled for the first time in four days and nights. They began to work faster to get the boat ready. They heaved on the cable with twice the strength, twice the speed. There would be no need to go to the Scilly Islands, after all, this wind would take them to the Lizard. The breeze was freshening—freshening fast. Before four o'clock they were headed for the Lizard and cramming on every bit of canvas they could find. In addition to their normal rig they had put on an extra topsail and they were even using blankets as studding sails to capture every last breath of this astoundingly marvellous providential north-north-west wind, which was freshening all the time and was going to blow them, not to the treacherous rocks of Scilly, but home.

The Lizard was passed quite early in the day, and at nine that evening they were abreast of Dodman Point. Shortly after midnight they caught a glimpse of the Trinity House lightship now anchored three miles from the Eddystone, at four o'clock on Friday morning they passed Rame Head, and at six they anchored in Plymouth Sound.

A routine journey home from the Eddystone reef, which had started on Monday afternoon, had been completed by Friday morning. So ended Smeaton's first year's work. It may be wondered whether any architect in history ever had to endure so much before he could lay even one stone of his building.

CHAPTER SEVENTEEN

Second Working Season

THROUGHOUT the winter months the tempo of the work never slackened. There was much to be done in the work-yard if they were to be ready to take advantage of the first fine weather of the following summer.

In December consignments of stone began to arrive from Portland and the Cornish moorstone quarries. These stones, averaging 1½ tons in weight, arrived rough-cut to approximations of Smeaton's measurements, and then they had to be exactly trimmed to the sizes and dovetailed shapes he had so carefully worked out. They had not only to be cut, but grooved and bored, for reasons which will be clear when the building process is described; and in addition, they had to fit perfectly into one another. All this had to be done against the clock, and in the face of unpredictable difficulties of all kinds.

On one occasion a message was received from one of the Cornish quarries that they had been let down by the man who had undertaken to ship the stone. Valuable days were lost while Smeaton sent one of his own boats to collect it. There was a period when French privateers were active in the waters off Portland, and boatmen were refusing to risk the journey to Plymouth with loads of stone. This necessitated representations to the Admiralty who would promise to send an escort and then fail to do so.

The Navy press-gangs were a constant nuisance, and although the Admiralty had given specific instructions that men on Eddystone work were not to be taken, some of their Lordships' more enthusiastic subordinates had a habit of feigning ignorance of this, and there would be more fuss and delay getting the men released. Smeaton finally hit on an idea to dispose of this problem. He asked Robert Weston to have an impressive silver medallion struck that could be issued as a badge of immunity to every man working for him. This was done, and from then on there was little interference from the press-gangs.

Once there was labour trouble. The foreman Hill proved to be a trouble-maker, and Smeaton sacked him. Hill told Smeaton that if he went the whole of his working group would down tools and follow. Smeaton decided to call his bluff. He immediately summoned a meeting of the twelve men who had been working under Hill, told them that the foreman was going, and said that if any of them wished to do the same they were free to leave there and then. Only one man chose to do so. After this prompt action there were no more incidents of this kind.

Then a difficulty arose with the town authorities. Smeaton needed room to set out the wooden moulds which were the gauges for cutting the stones to the right size. The only way to ensure that each circular course of stones would fit like a jig-saw, was to fit the moulds together course by course, and this required a large floor. He asked if he might use the Guildhall, but the Mayor refused on the grounds that chalk-marks would ruin the floor. Nor was he allowed to use the Assembly Room, the only other suitable hall. Eventually he found a place, but more time had been wasted.

In addition to the preparation of the building materials there was plenty of other work to be done. A deeper channel had to be dredged in the approach to the work-yard pier in readiness for the boats that would be carrying the stone to the reef. New boats had to be built—boats of different sizes and shapes specially designed for the idiosyncrasies of Eddystone. While all this was proceeding, Smeaton had to find time— usually in the evenings when everyone else had finished for the day—to carry out an exhaustive series of experiments in cement.

Cement was obviously one of the crucial difficulties. The resinous mortars in common use at the time were not good enough, as they depended for their efficacy on being applied to surfaces that were dry. One thing the Eddystone never offered was a dry surface. What Smeaton had to evolve was a cement that would stick to a moist surface and harden without having first to become completely dry. After weeks of patient experiment he finally decided on a mixture of lime and the volcanic ash called pozzolana, which came from the neighbourhood of Vesuvius. But he arrived at this formula only after weeks of trial and error in which he travelled to many parts of the country testing samples of different types of lime. The technical detail of these experiments in cement has no place in this narrative, but it is one of the important documents in the history of building. And the result was still pathetic by the standards of the quick-drying cement that would be commonplace a century later.

It was valuable to have produced such a cement, but it was only a contribution to Smeaton's armament. It cannot too often be stressed that his great enemy was the sea. The crux of the builder's problem was how to secure the newly laid stone so as to be proof against the waves until such time as the cement had been given a chance to set. At all stages of building the lighthouse had to aspire to monolithic solidity. With this in mind Smeaton had decided on a number of additional aids.

First, there was the idea of dovetailing the stones. Secondly, in the waists of each stone he proposed to cut indents three inches wide, one inch deep. Into these recesses between adjacent stones would be driven two oak wedges, one with its thick end downwards, the other the opposite way round so that together they formed a lock. These wedges would finish off the effect of the dovetailing and ensure that no lateral movement between the stones was possible. But he well knew that the elimination of lateral movement was not enough: a Biscay swell could easily sweep away an entire course of stones if it could wash away the cement on which it rested and force its way underneath.

The third device, therefore, was designed to fasten every course to the one below it. This could be done by boring through each stone two holes in alignment with similar holes in the stone or stones below. Through these holes would be driven trenails of extra hard oak. These wooden nails could be additionally tightened by having splinters driven into them. The surplus would then be cut off to leave the upper surface of the course flat. When the trenails became wet they would expand and fit more tightly than ever. By this means it was hoped that as soon as a stone had been set, it would quite literally be nailed to the course below.

To prepare the stones for the wedges and the trenails meant days of careful work by the masons in the yard. This was the method. As soon as a course was completed it was laid out in the work-yard exactly as it would eventually be on the rock. The next course up was then laid out on the first, the holes being bored through both courses while they were in this position. The stones were then carefully labelled, numbered, and lettered so that they would reach the rock in the right order and the foreman could see at a glance where each had to go. Every stone in this building was a living identity with a name, rank, and number.

By the end of May 1757 everything was ready for the second season on the rock, everything, that is, except the weather. On 3 June the *Neptune Buss* made its ponderous waddling way to its summer mooring a quarter of a mile from the reef. The mooring buoy was fixed in position a few yards from the House rock, for use as required when the rock itself could not be approached. By 10 June wooden piles had been fixed at the place where the boats tied up to prevent them rubbing against the rocks, and Smeaton's main lifting tackle, a pair of sheers together with its windlass had been fixed on the rock.

The sheers consisted of two heavy wooden legs joined in such a way as to form an inverted V and held in position by guy ropes, a tackle-block being suspended from the apex. The lifting rope which passed through this block was operated by a windlass. It was a primitive but effective way of lifting great weights, and sailors still use it.

Having fixed the sheers in position, Smeaton tested it by hoisting a ship's longboat, filled with men, on to the rock. This was to be his hoist for getting the stones from the boats to the rock. A triangle, a similar contrivance but with three legs instead of two, would be used to lower the stones into their final position.

At eight o'clock in the morning of Sunday, 12 June, the first stone, a massive piece of moorstone weighing $2\frac{1}{4}$ tons, was hoisted out of the *Eddystone Boat* and set roughly in position in the first course of four stones, the lowest step of the six that would bring the foundation tapering concavely towards the higher part of the sloping rock. The stone was engraved 1757, and to Smeaton, Jessop, and the out-company who had rowed across early that morning from the *Neptune Buss* to execute this task, it was a moment they would remember all their lives. It was the first time they had lifted a stone from the pitching boat to the rock. It was exceptionally heavy. It was their first attempt at an operation that would later become simplified by familiarity. But just this once it seemed wonderful to have lifted the immense mass from a heaving boat to the position that it was destined to occupy for ever. It took a long time, nearly four hours, and then they saw that the tide was rising and they hurriedly secured it with chains to the iron stanchions that still remained from Rudyerd's old foundations, and withdrew to the *Neptune Buss* to refresh themselves and impatiently kill time until the next tide. On the evening tide they returned, bedded the stone in cement, drove the hard oak trenails through it into the rock below, and coated the cemented joints with plaster of Paris as a precaution against the wash of the sea with which the next tide would drench and harry it. On the following day the other three stones which completed this first foundation course were cemented and trenailed into position.

The day after that, boats arrived with the second course of thirteen stones. Enough of the tide remained to land five and set one properly before the wind freshened and it became dangerous for the boats to remain in the Gut any longer. The four loose stones and the lifting tackle had to be hurriedly secured to Rudyerd's old stanchions with chains brought for this purpose, and the boats with difficulty extricated themselves from the Gut. One returned to Plymouth, the other, with Smeaton on board, made for the *Neptune Buss*. Rowing with all their strength against the wind, it took Smeaton's party an hour and a half to cover the four hundred yards to the *Buss*.

They had to endure two days of rough seas in the extreme discomfort of the *Neptune Buss* before it was possible to get back on the rock, and then they were there only long enough to fix one more stone of the second course. Another four days of storm again confined them to the *Neptune Buss* and when, after that, they returned to the rock it was to find that five stones had been washed away.

This was the worst thing of all that could happen. To lose any of the precious, so carefully shaped catalogued stones, each with its numbered place in the plan, meant that work could not continue until exact replicas had been provided. Smeaton immediately set off for Plymouth, sought out the moulds of the five lost stones, and stood over his masons as they laboured to produce replacements. It took them two days, and on 23 June, just a week after the first stone of the second course had been set, Smeaton sailed from Plymouth with the five new stones. But after rowing all night they could get nowhere near the reef, and it was not until four days later that the stones could be landed. Thereafter the weather improved, and they were able to work every tide until the evening of 30 June, when the second course was at last completed.

It was June and it had taken eighteen days and nights to set the seventeen stones of which these first two courses consisted. Smeaton, as equable as ever, said that this rate of progress did not dishearten him. The first two courses, so close to the low-water level of the sea, were bound to be the worst. And what was really good was to have discovered in extreme conditions that the trenails worked. Despite the battering they had received so soon after they had been set, none of the stones that had been trenailed had been dislodged. This was the important thing: not the fact that it had taken eighteen days to set seventeen stones.

This was the start of something which would go on for the rest of the summer, and through the following summer, and the summer after that. It would become a little easier as the building progressed, because every foot that it rose above the level of the water it was a foot easier to do this work. But it would never be easy, for the sea was an opponent which did not give up. It would never stop throwing its limitless weight against them. It would ensure that they were wet and miserable every minute they worked. It would taunt them by holding up for days the boats bringing them the stones with which they had to build. It would sap their spirit by turning the *Neptune Buss* into a pitching, sodden hell. The ocean's cold impersonal power would strike this building night and day. The laying of every single stone would be an end in itself, and one thousand four hundred and ninety-three stones would have to be set before the building was completed. One thousand four hundred and ninety-three times they would go through a procedure that even time, in these circumstances, could not make very much easier. And the sea would fight them to the bitter end.

From Plymouth in the smaller boats came the heavy stones, meticulously shaped and cut and drilled, and numbered to show their exact position in the building. The boats would tie up alongside the *Neptune Buss*, or at the mooring buoy near the rock, or if the sea was calm they might just ride at anchor. But always they were near so that a supply of stones was always at hand. As required, they would enter the Gut and tie up at the landing place.

The straining sheer-legs, leaning far over the breast of the rock, would hoist a stone from the tossing boat, depositing it on the rock or transferring it to the three-legged hoisting tackle they called the triangle. The triangle dangled the stone immediately above the place where it was to be set. As the stone hung there the cement was spread and the stone was gently lowered into it. There it was levelled under the eyes of Smeaton or Jessop with a spirit-level and beaten with a heavy wooden mallet until they were satisfied that it was sufficiently embedded in exactly the right place.

Now began the race against the ocean. On no account must the stone be allowed to move by even a fraction of an inch. Crouching with his back to the deluge of spray, a waiting carpenter inserted two wedges in the grooves at the sides of the stone, the first wedge head down, the second with the sharp end downwards, tapping them gently with an iron bar so as not to disturb the stone; then tapping a little harder until the wedges had locked themselves and the stone to its neighbour. What remained above the surface was then sawn off and liquefied mortar was poured into the cavity to fill any air space that might remain in the groove. The solid part of the mortar immediately sank and the stones soaked up much of the water. The process was repeated. Always the solid part of the mortar would sink, displacing some of the liquid already in the recess, and in this way the recess was finally filled with solid mortar to the bottom. Already the sea was half beaten. Now one of the tinners would step forward to drive a trenail through the heart of this stone into the one below—and then another. And if one of the trenails was at all loose in its hole, a wedge would be driven in to widen it, and when this had been done the projecting remainder would be cut off. It was at this point that Smeaton knew that the stone was safe. The Atlantic could now do its worst. It could not break these oak sinews binding every stone to the one below. But they would have to do this one thousand four hundred and ninety-three times before the work was done.

They had to work fast as well as accurately. The ocean never rested. From the moment the great stone had been lowered into the cement the waves came smashing against the rocks, drenching the workmen, striking the newly laid stone. But somehow they must keep their balance and their heads and their skill and, perched precariously on this tiny treacherous wave-swept platform, work as meticulously as if they were in the yard in Plymouth.

By the middle of July the third course of twenty-five stones had been fixed, and work had started on the fourth. Each of the two working companies having now had consider-able experience of what was required, Smeaton felt confident enough to return to Plymouth for a few days, leaving Jessop in charge on the rock. It was as well that he did. He was greeted with the news that two boats laden with stone for the Eddystone had been awaiting a favourable wind to bring them from Portland to Plymouth when their entire crews were seized by a press-gang, although they had been provided with Admiralty protections. This meant yet another protest to the Admiralty, who, as always, were sympathetic and promised to take action, though they seemed curiously powerless to restrain their junior officers from disobeying their orders in this matter. After some delay the Portland boatmen were released and the stone reached its destination. The second half of July began with several days of gales, but in spite of the time lost

on this account, the twenty-three stones of the fourth course
had been set by the end of the month, and five days later the
fifth course (twenty-six stones) had been completed. A week
of perfect weather made it possible to finish the sixth course
(thirty-two stones) by 11 August.

This was a milestone in the work, as the sixth course brought
the foundation up to the level of the top of the rock. Not only
had they gained eight precious feet of height above the sea,

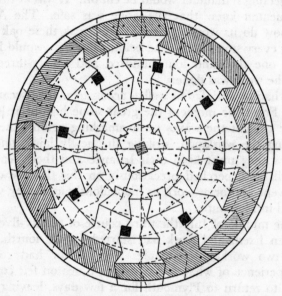

Typical floor-course showing dovetailed stones. Dotted lines represent
course above; black squares are marble joggles; black dots, trenails.

but from now on they would be constructing circular courses
on a level base. That meant that the most difficult part of the
task was now behind them. It had taken sixty-one days to lay
the 123 stones of the six foundation courses. Smeaton's methods
had been fully vindicated. But with the first circular course,
the seventh, he introduced yet another device to ensure
absolute rigidity from the moment of setting.

In addition to the wedges between the sides of adjacent stones
and the trenails that fastened each to the one below, he proposed to bind the courses together vertically with nine heavy

joggles, marble plugs one foot square. These joggles were sunk
into each course so that half their length projected above it.
The course above had nine holes cut in it to take the upper
half of the joggles. One joggle was set in the centre of each
course, the other eight were set equidistantly around it about
three feet from the outer edge.

There was a reason for this additional measure other than
the characteristic Smeaton determination to leave nothing to
chance. The firmness of the foundation courses had been
helped by the fact that the stones were cemented into the dovetails cut into the rock itself. The main circular courses of the
building would not have this extra support. The joggles were
to make up for this. Now the courses of the lighthouse would be
bound into a coherent whole not only by the scores of oak
sinews provided by the trenails, but by a bone structure of
heavy marble. Nothing was going to shift this building if
Smeaton could help it.

The building of the seventh course began well, the weather
for once being perfect for several days running. Then it
changed, and it was nearly a month before this course was
finished on 5 September. Yet, so wayward is Eddystone
weather, the eighth course was finished in five days and rapid
progress was made with the ninth, until gales again inter-
rupted the work. In the end the ninth course took eighteen
days to finish. These timings speak for themselves. Having
completed three courses above the foundation, and raised his
building another four and a half feet Smeaton decided to end
the work on the rock for that summer.

Considering all things, they had achieved a great deal in the
four months. The weather as usual had been infuriating, but
they had much to show for their labours. The worst was behind them. When they returned next year they would continue to have to work soaked to the skin, but they had grown
used to that. They would continue to row into and out of the
Gut with their hearts in their mouths, certain that this time
the turbulent waters in that vicious little channel must drive
them against the rocks. They would spend many more miserable days and nights on the hated *Neptune Buss* waiting for tides
to turn and the waves to become stilled and allow them to

row across to the reef only a quarter of a mile away and work
for a few hours—or perhaps only half an hour. But they had
finished for this season, and they had the winter in which to
forget about tides and gales and ground-swells. And every
man knew that there had been grafted on to the red rocks a
foundation that they would find next summer exactly as they
had left it.

It had been hard, dangerous, and uncomfortable, and one
tide's work was much like another, but there had been days to
remember: like the day Smeaton stepped back into one of the
joggle holes, stumbled, and went crashing down the sloping
rock on to his back. Luckily his injuries amounted to no more
than bruises and a badly dislocated thumb. Ruefully aware of
how long it might take to sail back to Plymouth and find a
doctor, he shut his eyes and pulled on the thumb with all his
considerable strength. To his relief it clicked back into place,
but his hand was painfully inflamed and useless for a month.
There was the day they found themselves working eerily in
thick fog and suddenly saw a sail on the adjacent reef. Lost in
the fog, the *Charming Sally*, a 130-ton brig from Bideford, had
mistaken the reef for a group of fishing-boats and run on to the
rocks before the crew of seven could take to their boat. Seven
very shaken boatmen, as relieved as they were astonished to find
a rescue party so conveniently on hand, were dispatched to the
Neptune Buss to be fed and revived, before being sent back to
Plymouth.

There was the sunny day that a great fleet of over a hundred
large merchant ships sailed majestically past, some bound for
America, the others for the Mediterranean. Smeaton was not
much given to expressions of emotion, but on this occasion he
could not forbear to note the feeling of satisfaction it gave him
to know that by the time many of those magnificent ships
returned he would have contributed to the safety of their
homecoming.

By early October all men, equipment, and boats were back
in Plymouth.

CHAPTER EIGHTEEN

Third and Fourth Working Seasons

SMEATON spent most of the winter in London, leaving the work-yard in Jessop's charge. When he returned to Plymouth in March 1758 the stone for the rest of the building had been fully prepared, and it was possible to pay off most of the masons. The third working season on the rock began on 2 July, and four days later the tenth course had been completed—but, the July storms running true to form, the eleventh took a fortnight. The twelfth course took six days, the thirteenth twelve, the fourteenth three—an indication of the persistent variability of even summer weather at Eddystone—but with the completion of the fourteenth course on 8 August another important milestone had been reached. This course twelve feet above the top of the rock completed the solid part of the tower.

The next ten courses had to allow for the entrance door and a central well, five feet in diameter, to accommodate the staircase. It took just over a month to complete them, and when on 24 August they were finished, the back of the task had been broken. With the late August weather as stormy as it had been the previous summer this would have been a convenient point at which to break off, leaving the upper part of the tower, consisting of four rooms and the lantern, for the following summer.

But it occurred to Smeaton that if he could complete the lowest of the four rooms, the store-room, it might be possible to fix the triangle on the roof with a lantern suspended from the block—and so provide a light a year ahead of schedule. The sturdy triangle, firmly lashed down, would be suitable for this purpose. Feeling rather pleased with himself, he asked the men for a special effort to complete this additional work before the weather finally broke; found two workmen willing, for double their normal wages, to spend the winter in the incom-

163

plete building looking after the light; and sent, through the proprietors, a formal application to Trinity House for permission to proceed with these arrangements. He was so confident of their approval that he went ahead without waiting for their reply, and by the end of September the store-room was complete except for the last few stones of the ceiling. But he reckoned without the inflexibility of the Corporation, to whom it apparently meant little that Smeaton's enterprise would make a light possible a year ahead of expectations.

They told him stiffly that 'on reading the acts of Parliament, the application from the merchants and owners of ships, the patent for the floating light, and the enclosed narrative of the first lighthouse erected there, they are of opinion that a light cannot be exhibited on the Eddystone rock till the lighthouse is rebuilt'.

As storms were now delaying the setting of the last stones of the store-room ceiling, Smeaton abruptly ended the season's work when the *Neptune Buss* broke away from its moorings one night and, after disappearing for two days, finally showed up in Dartmouth very much the worse for wear and with a complement of drenched and hungry men who were more than eager to forget all about the accursed Eddystone and everything to do with it until the next summer. Smeaton again left the workyard in the care of his assistants and spent the winter in London supervising the construction of the lantern and other metal fittings.

The fourth and last season on the rock began on 5 July, 1759. From now on the work would be much easier. Not only were there many fewer stones to be set in this hollow part of the structure, but the tower could now accommodate small numbers of workmen. But this last phase of the building presented two new problems. The circular rooms, twelve feet four inches in diameter, allowed for a wall thickness of twenty-six inches. Smeaton proposed to provide the whole of this thickness with single stones, sixteen of them making up each circular course. In order that the rooms would be as dry as possible he decided to use the impermeable moorstone for the wall. As it was not possible to cut these massive blocks of this particular granite into accurate dovetails, some other method had to be found of bonding them together. The method he decided upon was to lock adjacent stones together with joggles and iron clamps.

The second problem was created by the heavy floors, concave on their undersides. As can be seen in the sectional drawing of the lighthouse, these floors were fixed into the wall by two flanges which rested in two grooves cut into it—each flange fitting into a different course of stones. The curvature of the floor would cause it to exert a considerable outward strain on the wall at the point of junction, and some way had to be found of counteracting this. Smeaton recalled that Sir Christopher Wren had overcome a similar difficulty with the dome of St. Paul's Cathedral by binding the area of strain with circumferential chains leaded into the stone. He would do the same.

A groove four inches wide was cut into the top of the courses into which the flanges of the ceiling were to be placed. Eight endless chains the exact length and width of these circular grooves were brought out from Plymouth. Heavily greased against the rust of time, they were set in the grooves and molten lead was then poured into them. It took eleven hundredweight to fill them, and when the lead had hardened, stone and chain and lead were one. Where the massive floors would press downwards and outwards, straining to burst the building open, they would be hugged by two great chains sealed into the heart of the wall and now an organic part of it.

Room by room the tower soared rapidly towards completion, and with the end in sight the men put new heart into the work and smiled as they worked. The last ladles of lead hissed into a floor groove to seal up the last of the great binding chains. The highest room of all, the bedroom, was finished. Stone by stone they completed the lantern platform and the overhanging cornice designed to deflect outwards the giant waves that gales to come would send hurtling up the tower to savage the lantern. On 16 August the tower was finished. From the centre of the manhole on its crown Smeaton hung a plumb-line thirty-five feet down to the top of the solid. Without comment he noted that the tapering upper half of his seventy-foot structure was slightly out of perpendicular—by one-eighth of an inch.

It was now a race against time to complete the lantern and

M

balcony rails. The weather was deteriorating as it usually did towards the end of August. Trinity House wanted to know when the light would be lit. They asked for a firm date at least a week in advance so that they could advertise it. Smeaton gave them 16 October. That night for certain there would be a light.

With final triumph so near a series of petty setbacks now threatened the work. An epidemic of colic deprived Smeaton of several key workmen. At a time when he was needed on the rock night and day he was told that Prince Edward Duke of York was in Plymouth and wished to be shown the models and plans of the lighthouse by the builder. It was an honour, he admitted, but a nuisance at this particular time. The carrier who, in order to avoid the uncertainties of sea travel, had been hired to bring the lantern from London by road had chosen to leave most of it in Exeter. As work on the cupola was nearing completion in the yard, the foreman of the copper-smiths was taken ill.

Joiners, smiths, plumbers, glaziers, painters, and copper-smiths had now taken over the rock from the tinners and masons. Illness kept striking first one, then another. Whenever the weather allowed, Smeaton was out there with them, working rather harder than anyone, and always attending himself to any fitting that was of particular importance. Once during this time he was overcome by the fumes of a charcoal fire in which he was heating metal bars in the upper store-room. Workmen found him unconscious on the floor of the room below, and it took them some time to bring him round, and then he could remember nothing of what had happened. Luckily he was tough and emerged from this experience with nothing worse than bruises and a bad fright, though for some minutes the workmen were convinced that he was dead.

Despite these mishaps, the work was forced ahead. By the beginning of October the iron cross-bars of the windows were in position; the copper funnel from the kitchen fireplace had been fixed; the glazing of the lantern was completed and the cupola was in position above it, surmounted by a gilt ball—Smeaton's one modest concession to non-functional decoration. He screwed this into place himself because it would have to withstand the full force of the wind, and he would not entrust so vulnerable a fixture to anyone else.

A lead-strip lightning conductor was run down the side of the tower to the rocks. Tackle for raising and lowering the chandelier was installed. When this had been done candles were lit to test the ventilation of the lantern and the glass was polished to a high gloss with jeweller's rouge.

On 8 October the keepers were given their final instructions in case the weather prevented Smeaton getting back to the tower to light up on 16 October. It had been suggested that he should engrave his name in a suitably prominent position inside the tower, but he refused, arranging instead for the following two inscriptions to be cut. In the wall of the upper store-room a quotation from the 127th Psalm: 'Except the Lord build the house, they labour in vain that build it'; and in the stone above the lantern door, the last to be set in place, '24th Aug 1759. Laus Deo'.

Shortly before dusk on 16 October, 1759 the three keepers— Henry Edwards, Henry Carter, and John Hatherley—climbed into the lantern and lit for the first time the new Eddystone light. Smeaton, prevented by rough weather from joining them at this climactic moment, watched from Plymouth Hoe and saw the light quite clearly through his telescope.

The work—completed without a single fatality or serious injury—had taken three years, nine weeks, and three days from the first cutting of the rock to the display of the light; but the time spent on the rock totalled less than sixteen weeks. The lighthouse consisted of 1,493 pieces of stone weighing 988 tons which had been locked, wedged, plugged, and cemented into monolithic oneness by more than 700 marble joggles, 1,800 thick oak trenails, and 4,500 oak wedges. It cost £40,000.

A lighthouse had been planned and had methodically taken place. Smeaton believed that it would last for ever, not because he was boastful but because he considered that it had been scientifically designed to pit weight, strength, and cohesion against the power of the wind and the waves, and every part of it had been properly built.

At this distance of time it seems a little pathetic that the net result of this prodigious effort was the suspension of twenty-four six-pound tallow candles seventy feet above the rocks. But the yellow glare which they created was said to be visible with the naked eye more than five miles away. For the time being it was enough. If this tower could resist the fury of the ocean, the reef would once again be safe. Twenty-four candles were the difference between life and death.

The lighting of the new Eddystone caused a great stir in the West Country, and this would probably have spread to London and the country at large had the occasion not happened to coincide with news that was bound to excite the popular imagination more.

On 14 October the nation had been plunged into gloom by the publication of the depressing dispatch which General Wolfe had sent to Pitt on the eve of Quebec. Written from a sick-bed, the report gave an account of a severe military reverse and a hopeless situation of stalemate that seemed to have resulted from it. Only three days later, on 17 October, came the electrifying news of the great victory on the Heights of Abraham and the young general's dramatic death at the battle's victorious climax. London went mad. Guns were fired, bonfires lit, flags flown from every high point. The sky was alive with fireworks and people danced in the streets and sang and toasted one another all night in the taverns. It is not surprising that the lighting of Eddystone between these two fateful dates was scarcely noticed except in the neighbourhood of Plymouth.

This no doubt was why it was possible for the modest Smeaton to disappear quietly and for the time being largely unsung to take up again the threads of his old humdrum work repairing bridges, canals, mills, and docks; installing pumps; planning drainage schemes.

Before leaving Plymouth, however, he visited the lighthouse once or twice and spent some time observing its behaviour, either from a boat when the weather permitted, or through his telescope from the Hoe. It was through the telescope that one morning he watched heavy seas totally submerging the tower, and waves occasionally rising high above it. He had disbelieved Winstanley's more dramatic estimates of the height to which the waters flew above the tower. Now he wasn't so sure and this impression was supported by a letter he received at his

RUDYERD'S TOWER ON FIRE, 1755

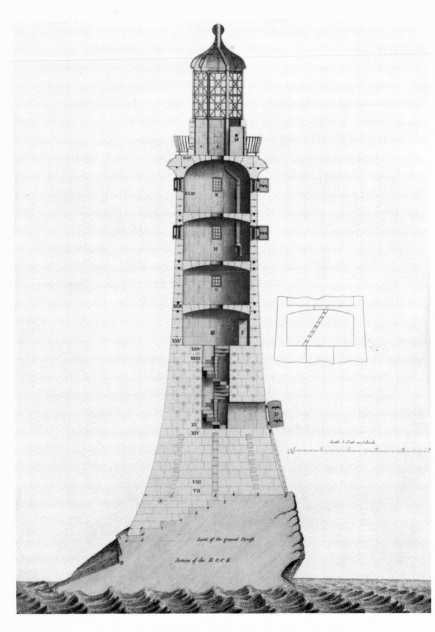

SMEATON'S TOWER AT LOW WATER

Marble joggles interlocking the courses are indicated by small darker squares

home near Leeds four months later. It was from the youngest of the three keepers, John Hatherley, and had been written after twelve days of gales in which the waves had constantly run over the top of the tower.

> The house did shake as if a man had been up in a great tree. The old men were frighted almost out of their lives, wishing they had never seen the place, and cursing those that first persuaded them to go there. The fear seized them in the back but rubbing them with oil and turpentine gave them relief.

In between rubbing his elderly colleagues' backs, the admirable Hatherley had kept the light going every night, and the only damage was the smashing of one pane of glass in the lantern by a particularly fierce wave. The hole was quickly closed with one of the heavy wood panels provided for the purpose.

Smeaton was also responsible, before leaving Plymouth, for an important administrative innovation which guided the provisioning of lighthouses until modern times. During his contact with the service he had learned that it was a recurring complaint of the light keepers that they frequently ran short of food and were compelled to eat the candles. This had become a perpetual grumble throughout the lighthouse service and two solutions were being canvassed.

The first was that keepers should be paid more than the £25 a year they were then receiving, so that they could provision themselves better. The second was that they should be victualled by Trinity House and the other lighthouse owners. Smeaton rejected both. The wages, he conceded, were not excessive, but they were higher than those of the average country workmen of the day, while the basic domestic expenses of lighthouse keepers were obviously much less. As for the second suggestion, he said it was well known that when food had been provided by owners, the keepers had dropped into the habit of exchanging much of it for liquor and had then pretended that it had gone bad and that they had had to throw it into the sea: capping this with the dramatic lament that they had been saved from starvation only by eating the candles.

Smeaton's own solution reflected the shrewdness that he had

shown in managing his labour force during the building. The only way to avoid embezzlement, he considered, was to retain the principle that the men were responsible for buying their own provisions. To ensure at the same time that they were always adequately fed, he proposed the following system. Every six months the owners should stock up the lighthouse with enough food to last that period and the men draw on this as required and pay for what had been used up at the six-monthly stocktaking. As a concession, they would pay only the wholesale price of the food. By this means they would be better off than if they bought the food themselves on land, and embezzlement would be impossible. The Eddystone proprietors adopted this system, which later spread to other lighthouses.

The principle that keepers victual themselves survives to the present day, and is almost ritually embedded in lighthouse tradition. At every monthly relief the keepers of a rock light-house receive the stores they ordered at the time of the previous relief. They pay for them when they next go ashore them-selves. The food stock of each keeper is stored separately, and before each meal he selects what he is personally going to use. Experience has shown that this is the only way when men of varying tastes and temperament are isolated from the world in such cramped intimacy. So sacred is the principle that when the small round table is set for a meal, it is automatic to place on it three packets of sugar, three packets of butter, three loaves of bread, three pots of jam. No man will dream of touching another's. Each will have told the one acting for the day as cook what he wishes to eat as his main dish, and seldom will two be eating the same.

Circumstances and details are different, but essentially this tradition goes back to Smeaton. Generations of keepers have found it one of the greatest aids to the maintenance of happy relations—the biggest single problem in the running of a light-house.

Eddystone was a long way from Gray's Inn, where Smeaton did much of his work, and even farther from Yorkshire. But he kept in touch through correspondence, and when the opportunity arose he liked to revisit Plymouth. An assignment in Cornwall gave him a chance to do this in 1761. He found the tower clean and in good order, its lower half now heavily coated with marine vegetation and limpets, so that more than ever it seemed a natural growth on the rock.

Smeaton was not the only distinguished visitor to the Eddystone that summer. A visit to the lighthouse was becoming one of the standard excursions which Plymouth liked to arrange for its illustrious guests. In July the town was visited by its most famous living son, Sir Joshua Reynolds, and the painter had invited his friend Dr. Johnson to accompany him as his guest. Johnson greatly enjoyed himself in Plymouth. It was at a dinner party there, that he jauntily replied: 'Ignorance, pure ignorance!' to the lady who asked him why he had incorrectly defined the word *pastern* in his dictionary. Plymouth gave Johnson a warm reception, and the Commissioner of the Naval Dockyard placed the Admiralty yacht at his disposal for a trip to the Eddystone with Reynolds. As might be expected, the Eddystone was less hospitable than Plymouth. They were able to approach quite close to the lighthouse, but the sea was too rough for a landing. It is a matter of regret that Boswell was not present. Eight or nine hours of conversation between Johnson (a bad sailor) and Reynolds in a Biscay swell would have been worth having.

Early the following year the lighthouse endured a testing which satisfied even the most sceptical that it was there to stay. There seem at all times to have been a number of gloomy Plymouth men whose first reaction to any bad weather was to shake their heads and assert that the Eddystone would not be there on the following morning. The terrible gale of January 1762 brought them all out of hiding. The harbours and quayside were devastated. Six large merchant ships were destroyed at their moorings in the harbour. Six out of eight warships in the Sound were dismasted. Piers and jetties were washed away. One ship was flung ashore into a house, which it demolished. Mountainous waves swept over the quayside, flooding the shops to the height of their counters. In a few hours £80,000 worth of damage was done. 'If the Eddystone survives this', a man was heard to say, 'it will be there till the Day of Judgment.' Many of Smeaton's friends admitted later that they had been anxious. One of them, Dr. Mudge, wrote him a letter immediately afterwards, describing the storm, and telling him how relieved he had been to see the gilded ball still there when the wind had died down on the following morning.

As soon as it was possible to make contact with the lighthouse, the keepers were asked to report the damage and their requirements for immediate repairs. They replied that the tower had suffered no damage at all: not even a single pane of glass had been broken. But they would like a pot of putty to plug some gaps in the cement which had developed the previous summer and were now rather worse. Eddystone keepers no longer had to rub the terror out of their backs with turpentine. They knew this tower now, knew what it was made of and what it could stand. It had transferred to them its own confidence. It was theirs. It was where they lived. It was how they lived. It was their life.

Smeaton's next visit was in 1766, when he carried out a complete inspection of the lighthouse. Again he was pleased to find that there were no serious faults. But he did notice one thing—the effect of a heavy sea on the cavernous mouth at the end of the House rock. As the waves struck this opening they seemed to penetrate to the very heart of the rock on which the lighthouse stood. The noise was frightening, and when the seas were particularly heavy not only the lighthouse but the rock itself perceptibly shuddered. The keepers had referred to this from time to time but this was the first occasion on which he had experienced it himself.

> Whether this cavity in the rock may ever prove of any detriment to the building is not to be determined with certainty: all that can be said is that hitherto it does not seem to have been of any hurt thereto. I could undertake to fill it up and make it solid at the expence of about £250 besides my own attendance if it was thought worth the charge.

Either he thought no more about it or the proprietors considered that it was not worth the charge. Anyway nothing was done. He did not visit the lighthouse again for eleven years, when business in the West Country enabled him to fit in a brief visit in 1777. Most of the old hands who had helped in its building were now dead. There was still no difficulty, he found, in recruiting keepers, though the pay was still only £25 a year. The work appealed to retired seamen, and there were always half a dozen names on the waiting-list whenever a vacancy occurred, which, significantly, was seldom. During this visit the keepers told him of the tragi-comic circumstances in which one of their number had died a year or two previously. This man had served on the Eddystone for fourteen years. He enjoyed the life so much that in the last two years of his time he refused to take his shore leave, giving it up to one or other of his colleagues. He intended to do this for the third year running, but was persuaded to have a spell ashore. The impact of the outside world proved disastrous after his two years of isolation. Though by nature a quiet sober man, he went straight to a beerhouse and became drunk, in which condition he remained for the rest of his month's leave.

He had to be carried to the boat that was to return him to the lighthouse, the boatmen hoping that the journey would sober him up. But at the end of it there was no sign of recovery. They helped him into the lighthouse, where he continued in his drunken stupor for three days and then died.

Smeaton visited the lighthouse for the last time in 1787. He was now sixty-three and had given up active work to write accounts of some of his more important works, including the building of the Eddystone. For relaxation he still devoted himself to experiments in his workshop at Austhorpe Lodge. He died in 1792 and was buried in the parish church in Whitkirk.

John Smeaton was a practical visionary who by a combination of instinct, study, and painfully dedicated experiment laid many of the foundations of British engineering practice. He retained to the last his passion for experiment, his modesty, his simplicity, his Yorkshire accent. He was indifferent to money beyond what he considered reasonable to his needs and his idea of basic comfort. His fee remained the same to the end of his working career—'two guineas for a full day's work'—and as there is no record of what he was paid for the Eddystone, it is reasonable to assume that he charged no more than his normal fee for the three and a half years he devoted to it, which works out at about seven hundred guineas a year. It does not seem excessive when it is remembered that he gave up all other work for this single task.

He was once approached by the Princess Dashkoff, who offered him great financial inducements to go to Russia and work for Catherine the Great. When her largest offer had been refused the Princess took her leave with these words:

> Sir, I honour you. You may have your equal in abilities, perhaps: but in character you stand alone. The English minister, Sir Robert Walpole, was mistaken and my Sovereign has the misfortune to find one man who has *not* his price.

Smeaton believed that work was its own reward and money of secondary importance. He believed, too, that ability carried with it an obligation to others. 'The abilities of the individual', he once said, 'are a debt due to the common stock of public well-being.' It is one thing to believe this: Smeaton can truly be said to have lived up to it.

His Forth–Clyde canal, the Ramsgate Harbour scheme, and a number of other projects were major works in their own right, but the Eddystone overshadows everything else that he did as a supreme feat of creative engineering. That he was not again called upon to execute any work of comparable difficulty and grandeur is a reflection of the age in which he lived. The time was not yet ripe for the creative engineer. But it would be wrong to say that Smeaton was born ahead of his time. His value is that he *was* born during this barren lull before the great industrial storm of the nineteenth century. When that storm broke and made a new world in which the genius of the engineer could flower as creatively as that of the artist, greater men than Smeaton would come on the scene—Brunel, Rennie, Telford, Watt, the English Stephensons, and the Scottish Stevensons. But they would only be greater because John Smeaton had gone before and they would have the advantage of starting where he had left off.

Two of them at least had the grace to acknowledge the debt. James Watt, who always referred affectionately to Smeaton as 'Father' Smeaton, paid him this tribute:

In justice to him we should observe that he lived before Rennie, and before there were one-tenth of the artists there are now. His example and precepts have made us all engineers.

This was what Robert Stephenson, the railway engineer, had to say about him in 1858:

Smeaton is the greatest philosopher in our profession this country has yet produced. He was indeed a great man, possessing a truly Baconian mind, for he was an incessant experimenter. The principles of mechanics were never so clearly exhibited as in his writings, more especially with respect to resistance, gravity, the power of water and wind to turn mills, and so on. His mind was as clear as crystal, and his demonstrations will be found mathematically conclusive. To this day there are no writings so valuable as his in the highest walks of scientific engineering; and when young men ask me, as they frequently do, what they should read I invariably say 'Go to Smeaton's philosophical papers; read them, master them thoroughly, and nothing will be of greater service to you.' Smeaton was indeed a very great man.

The final importance of Smeaton is that, like the beacon he erected in the open sea, he shines in solitary splendour above the technological sterility of eighteenth-century Britain, lighting the way to the wonders of the nineteenth.

It is fitting that in creating his masterpiece, which so perfectly reflected the ideals of labour, service, and beauty, he happened also to build a lasting personal memorial to everything he believed and loved.

CHAPTER NINETEEN

New Developments

SMEATON'S Eddystone introduced the modern era of the lighthouse, but there was no immediate rush to follow his example. Back in 1700 the 2,350 miles of English and Welsh coastline had been lit by eleven lighthouses. By 1780 the number had crept up to only twenty-five, of which a mere five were built and controlled by Trinity House. Most of them were extremely primitive. The private owners varied both in their standards of efficiency and in the charges they levied. Although for more than forty years it could rest on its laurels as the only rock lighthouse, the Eddystone, like the others, was distinctly variable in its service. The original proprietors were long since dead, and their heirs had inherited the income without the sense of responsibility or even of interest that should have gone with it. As late as 1807 the lighthouse was still lit by twenty-four candles, though more modern equipment had long been installed elsewhere. But in the closing years of the eighteenth century there were signs of an awakening, and it was helped along by two influences, one administrative, the other technical.

On the administrative side Trinity House at last decided to assume their proper stature and settle this lighthouse business once and for all. It has been seen that in the past the Corporation's attitude was often puzzling; on the one hand, insisting on their supreme authority, on the other, seeming to contradict this by leasing lighthouses to private owners for an annual rent. But in fairness it should now be made clear that there were two possible reasons for this apparent ambivalence.

First, it is evident that the proliferation of charters, acts, royal patents, and warrants that through the years had piled up in the Trinity House files had confused the issue of their precise function to the point where only lawyers could thrive

THE START OF DOUGLASS' TOWER

(above) Working on the foundations—Smeaton's tower in the background

(left) The Duke of Edinburgh lays the Foundation Stone, 1879. A view from Smeaton's tower

THE DOUGLASS WORKYARD AT PLYMOUTH

Trial assembly of courses before being sent to the rock

on it. There had been constant litigation with the private owners, and the fragmentary records that survive show that the courts were repeatedly called upon to define the Corporation's exact status and powers, but never satisfactorily succeeded in doing so. Sometimes they decided one way, sometimes another, but there never seemed to be a final answer. It may well be that the Brethren, growing weary of this, decided that it would save a lot of trouble to farm the lighthouses out. They were, after all, a non-profit-making body, and more than once the Courts had sharply reminded them that their function was strictly supervisory.

This view fits in with another theory advanced by D. Alan Stevenson. He points out that it was not until 1834 that Trinity House for the first time appointed to their organization a whole-time lighthouse engineer, and that until the end of the eighteenth century their main concern was with pilotage and all matters to do with shipping on the Thames—in addition to administering their various charities and trusts. Lighthouses probably meant relatively little to them up to this time. In which case it would not be so surprising that they should for many years have been glad to wash their hands of what they possibly regarded as something of a sideline, thereby saving themselves financial risk and interminable legal arguments with private owners, who could fight them with the support of the Monarch or of Parliament. It could account, for instance, for their leasing the Smalls lighthouse for £5 a year to a man whose heirs eventually derived from it an annual income of £11,000, though they might in due course have felt a little wistful about charging so small a rent.

By the turn of the century, however, the Corporation had had enough. The time had come to take charge and dispose of the anomalies of private ownership, which were a constant cause of complaint by shipowners who had to pay inconsistent dues for highly inconsistent standards of service. It would be many years before they gained complete control, but moves in this direction were now constant and effective.

There was a step towards rationalization in 1786, when an Act of Parliament divided the British Isles into three districts for lighthouse administration. Scotland and the Isle of Man were to be managed by the Commissioners for Northern Light-houses; Ireland by the Irish Lighthouse Board; England, Wales, and the Channel Islands by Trinity House. But it was also made clear that the other two authorities were answerable to Trinity House in all matters other than day-to-day manage-ment.

Finally, from this time on Trinity House would automatic-ally take over all English or Welsh lighthouses as their leases expired. It cannot be known whether this new determination had anything to do with the fact that William Pitt happened to be Master of Trinity House between 1790 and 1805. It was certainly welcome.

The new technical impetus came from across the Channel. While France was simmering towards her revolution, an engineer named Argand was perfecting a new type of oil-lamp on which he had been working for years. Others were experi-menting along similar lines, but it is Argand who is credited with having first made practicable the oil-lamp with a circular wick, creating its own air current inside a cylindrical glass. It was the French lighthouse engineer Teulère who took the Argand lamp a stage further by backing it with a parabolic reflector that would gather together the rays of this unpre-cedently bright lamp and project them forward in a beam.

From this it was a short step to the idea of arranging groups of such lamps around a circular framework, and later to making the framework revolve. If an apparatus of this kind were set up in the lantern of a lighthouse, three or more beams could be made to revolve, and the effect would be that from any given viewpoint the flashes of the turning beams would be followed by eclipses. The duration and frequency of flashes and eclipses could be varied according to the spacing of the lamps on the revolve.

This was the beginning of modern lighthouse illumination. First, the circular-wicked Argand lamp, brighter than any-thing previously known; secondly, the application of a reflector to concentrate and project the light in a beam; thirdly, the mounting of groups of these lights on a frame. Fourthly—but some time later—making the frame revolve. It was the start of the system which in its present-day form ensures that every

lighthouse is not only a beacon but an internationally identi-
fiable signal. By the type of flash, and its duration, and the
number of flashes and eclipses in a minute, the seaman, by
reference to his chart or pilot, can find out exactly which lighthouse he has sighted. Known as the catoptric system of
illumination, the reflected Argand took the lighthouse out of its
technical infancy. The tower at Dieppe was the first to be so
equipped in 1784, but it was not for several years that any
English lighthouses were converted to the new system, and then
only the ones managed by Trinity House. Whether the owners
were unaware of the new equipment or too mean to instal it is
not clear. More probably the latter: it could cost anything up
to £4,000. The Eddystone was still using candles twenty-three
years after the Argand had become available. It is indicative
of the attitude of some of the private owners that thirty-eight
years after Argand the St. Bees lighthouse in Cumberland could
still offer nothing better than coal fires—a form of illumination
which, so far from lighting the coast, more frequently increased
its obscurity with dense clouds of smoke.

In 1807 the ninety-nine year lease of the Eddystone expired
and Trinity House took over. The lighthouse had to take its
turn in the queue for conversion to the new illumination—the
Corporation had a continuous programme of conversion in
hand—but four years later the candles were at last replaced by
twenty-four Argand lamps fitted with reflectors. The cost was
more than £3,000, and with other repairs reduced the revenue
from the lighthouse for that year from a gross £6,722 to £3,271
—this income being derived from a duty of one penny a ton for
all English ships passing the light, twopence for what were
politely termed 'stranger' ships.

Meanwhile the creative initiative was passing for the time
being from England to Scotland. The chief engineer to the
Northern Lighthouse Board at the time was Robert Stevenson,
founder of a Scottish lighthouse dynasty that has continued to
the present generation. One of the few Stevensons (not to be
confused with the railway Stephensons of England) who did
not become a lighthouse engineer was Robert's grandson,
Robert Louis, though R. L. S. always shared the family
enthusiasm for the subject—as did another Scottish writer, Sir

Walter Scott, who adored visiting lighthouses and occasionally wrote fragments of indifferent verse in their visitors' books. Successive generations of Stevensons not only built some of Scotland's most famous lighthouses but, between them, produced most of the standard scientific and technical literature on the subject in the English language.

At the time Trinity House took over the Eddystone, Robert Stevenson was starting on the work which was to make him famous—the lighthouse on the submerged Inchcape Rock ten miles off the east Scottish coast opposite the Firth of Tay. Generations of children have compulsorily become familiar with Southey's *Ballad of Inchcape Rock*, which tells how the monks of Aberbrothock fitted a warning bell to this dangerous rock, and how the pirate Sir Ralph the Rover removed it to increase his prospect of victims but was himself trapped by the rocks for want of it. Hence the name Bell Rock, by which rock and lighthouse are more popularly known. It was an appallingly difficult feat of building, because the rock is barely uncovered even at the lowest of low tides. A temporary barrack for the workmen had first to be erected and then a coffer dam constructed and pumped dry before the foundations could be laid, and it was not easy to keep it dry in the face of the attentions of the open sea. The Bell Rock Lighthouse was much bigger than the Eddystone and took five years to complete. Stevenson was the first of the new stars who learned their ABC from the Eddystone Narrative of 'Father' Smeaton and applied to it the exciting new scientific and engineering developments that were now becoming available. But he longed to see the Eddystone and compare it with his own creation. He was able to do this in 1813.

At the beginning of the century he had already, as a very young man, made one tour of inspection of English lighthouses to study them for ideas and techniques before going to work on his own. He had seen twenty-five but, as might be expected, the Eddystone had defied his efforts to land on it. Now he asked Trinity House if he might make another tour. They were more than willing that he should do so, as there was no regular system of inspection in operation at the time, and it would be invaluable to them to have the critical comments of the leading British lighthouse expert of the day. In fact, he made two more tours: the first two years before the Battle of Waterloo, the other five years later. On both occasions he succeeded in landing on the Eddystone, but each time with extreme difficulty, and a considerable part of both reports is devoted to explaining just how difficult and frightening it had been to land on the rock and re-embark from it. These two reports are of great interest because they are the only existing accounts of how Smeaton's lighthouse impressed a visiting expert in its middle age.

Stevenson's first experience of the Eddystone was evidently something of a disappointment. He had been brought up on Smeaton, and no doubt the Eddystone had assumed a legendary stature in his imagination. He had endured a rough and un-nerving sail to reach it, and it was perhaps inevitable that when at last he was confronted by the actuality it seemed something of an anti-climax. It was much smaller than he had expected. Especially when compared with his own Bell Rock Lighthouse.

> From the tower being only about twenty-six feet diameter where it rises above the rock, while the Bell Rock tower diameter is forty-two feet, and from the height of the Eddystone being eighty-five to the top of the ball while the Bell Rock is about one hundred and twenty feet, the appearance of the Eddystone is rather diminutive to an eye accustomed to look at the Bell Rock.

He found its proportions disappointing.

> The elevation does not partake of that symmetry which the drawings represent but appears out of proportion. The base seems small for the height of the masonry, and above the balcony the parapet and lightroom likewise seem much too high for their diameter.

He was sharply critical of some of the constructional detail and also of the condition of parts of the building.

> The faces of the stones are in some instances wasting and the joints are extremely coarse and not neatly wrought. The light-room is small and confined and the light much obstructed by the cross bars. . . . There are three tiers of reflectors with a neat frame supporting twenty-four reflectors of silvered copper and

N

brass burners. The apparatus not in a very cleanly state. . . . The balcony rail has not been a good job. The doors and windows are ill-hung and ill-fitted and the ironwork much rusted.

There were three keepers in residence—the fourth being on shore leave—and they were paid £40 a year, with an extra allowance, unspecified, for food. They treated Stevenson to the usual chilling tales of how the waves came over the top of the lantern in heavy storms. Stevenson remarks that they were a little surprised when he pursued this point with some close questioning about the proportion of spray, as opposed to sea, that reached this height and wrung from them the admission that perhaps it was mostly spray that actually struck the lantern. The action of the waves had discoloured the outside of the tower which was a dirty greenish colour up to about thirty feet above the rock.

But the most significant sentence in Stevenson's report related not to the lighthouse but to the rock on which it stood.

Upon an inspection of the rock, it appears that the building might have been placed to advantage for the enlargement of the base perhaps eight feet more to the south-west, by which means the tower might have been got wholly upon the solid rock.

He could not fail to notice the undermining of the part of the rock on which the tower in fact stood: the deep cut of which Smeaton himself had remarked: 'Whether this cavity in the rock may ever prove of any detriment to the building is not to be determined with certainty. . . .' For fifty-four years it had been no detriment. But the keepers did speak of the 'shake' when heavy seas were pounding the opening.

When Stevenson visited the Eddystone for the second time five years later either the Trinity House engineers had been active or his mood was mellower.

The house seems to be in a very good state of repair and does not appear to have sustained any injury by the lapse of time. The joints are full of cement and the stones exhibit little appearance of decay . . .

These were the stones which five years previously he had described as 'in some instances wasting and the joints are

THE PRESENT LIGHTHOUSE
Completed by Douglass, 1882

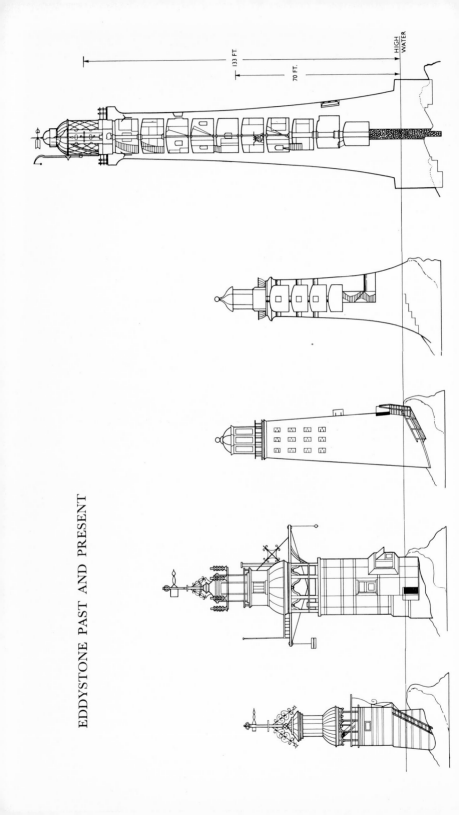

EDDYSTONE PAST AND PRESENT

133 FT.

70 FT.

HIGH WATER

extremely coarse and not neatly wrought'. It must have been a smoother sail to the rock the second time and without the sense of anti-climax at the end of it!

There was still, however, much to find fault with. The unnerving wooden ladder, suspended by a single rope, by which the entrance door was reached—it could easily, he said, have been replaced by iron steps. The windlass for hoisting stores was most awkwardly placed at the head of the stairway so that it was only with the greatest difficulty that he could get into the lowest room. The lantern, only eight feet in diameter, was 'very confined and much hampered by a useless heating apparatus'. The floor of the lantern was 'extremely dirty and sawdust is used to soak up the oil, and the whole is in the same filthy state as in 1813'.

Nor was he much taken with the keepers themselves, whose pay had risen to £50 p.a. since his last visit, with an allowance of £18 p.a. for food.

> The lightkeepers' duty is performed in a slovenly manner, but this is owing to the bad system in keeping lighthouses, or rather in inspecting them by agents, who cannot be supposed to know anything of the business when they do see it—and this, with Collectors of the Customs and such gentlemen, must be seldom.

The interior, in the opinion of Stevenson, left much to be desired.

> In the interior everything remains as when the tower was built. The stair is inconveniently narrow, the interior is too small and the whole furniture and apparatus is coarse, paltry and mean. But all this is no imputation to Smeaton as an engineer, as without the aid of the national purse or the funds of the Trinity Board, this could not be overtaken otherwise. Works of this kind are not to be looked for at the hands of a lessee.

Once again, however, the ominous part of the report related to the rock.

> It is shaken all through, and dips at a considerable angle . . . and being undermined for several feet it has rather an alarming appearance . . . were I connected with the charge of this highly important building . . . I should not feel very easy in my mind for its safety.

N 2

He estimated that the undermining of the rock penetrated to at least the circumference of the lighthouse base, and there must be considerable danger to the building if the sea succeeded in enlarging the cut and penetrating under the building itself. There was no evidence that it had succeeded in doing so since the lighthouse had been built. But the keepers *did* speak constantly of that terrifying shake when great seas hammered the rock from the south-west.

'I consider', Stevenson concluded ominously, 'the importance of this subject to be such as to require the immediate attention of the Trinity Board.'

Suddenly it seemed that time had overtaken the lighthouse that Smeaton built. It was an antique. A curiosity from a forgotten age. A curiosity, moreover, that was apparently resting on a perilous trap that might at any moment be sprung. For the undermining of the rock meant that the lighthouse—nearly one thousand tons of masonry—was pressing night and day on the sharply sloping upper jaw of a dragon's mouth. Night and day the Atlantic flung its limitless tons of water at the throat as it had done for millions of years. The hard gneiss was not easily eroded, but the formation of the rock at this vital junction point presupposed what a later age of geologists would define as a fault. An interruption in the consistency of strata. A point of eventual weakness, and if there was a weakness the sea would find it in the end, even if it took centuries. It might take centuries or it might happen at the next tide.

The tower's weight, on which Smeaton had counted to oppose the sea, would accelerate its downfall unless the rock held firm. The pressure and leverage of one thousand tons on a small upper jaw of rock would help the sea if eventually it found a weakness at the dragon's throat and by ruthless attrition succeeded in rubbing it away particle by particle —as now it was suspected of doing. Every time it pounded into the jaws of the petrified dragon mouth it gripped for a few seconds the base of the tower, titanically upheaving it. Would the throat hold out for ever? Nobody would say it would *not*. But the keepers insisted that the shake was getting worse.

Nevertheless, it defiantly continued to survive, and in 1824 showed that it could still take the worst that the Atlantic could throw against it. November of that year produced one of the worst recorded gales, and this is an extract from the Principal Keeper's log:

> The sea was tremendous, and broke with such violence on the top and round the building as to demolish in an instant five panes of the lantern glass and sixteen cylinder glasses the former of which is of unusual thickness. The house shook with so much violence as to occasion considerable motion of the cylinder glasses fixed in the lamps and at times the whole building appeared to jump as if resting on an elastic body. The water came from the top of the building in such quantities that we were overwhelmed, and the sea made a breach from the top of the house to the bottom.

But the following morning the lighthouse was still there.

The nineteenth century was now getting into its stride. The tidal wave of technological progress was gaining momentum, and this was reflected in the lighting of the seas as it was in other spheres. Machines made it easier to build better. In 1822 a revolutionary new development in illumination was perfected and once more it came from France. Augustin Fresnel produced something far better than the reflector. Instead of reflecting the light from behind, he devised a means of setting before it a panel made up of a central lens surrounded by several concentric circles of prisms, so echeloned that the panel as a whole sucked in the rays of light, bent or refracted them into a single beam, and in the process vastly magnified their power. This system, the dioptric system of illumination, is the basis of that in use today. Only the lamp itself has changed. The Dutch were the first to follow the French and adopt the new system. The Stevensons were not slow to introduce it to Scotland, adding a considerable amount of new research and development of their own. Trinity House took it up. The ability to bend and concentrate and magnify light on an unprecedented scale was a tremendous stimulus to the lighthouse engineers. It was no longer a question of getting any light at all showing in some inaccessible place, but of sweeping the ocean with mighty beams hitherto undreamed of.

The great new lighthouses that now began to go up more than ever made the Eddystone seem diminutive, insignificant, a survival from the past. But its light was still good, though it was too small to accommodate the new lenticular equipment. And it was still there.

There were other technical advances. The Stevensons and others at home and abroad were turning the construction of lighthouses into a science. Smeaton had given them the grounding. Now, a century wiser, they could substitute knowledge and certainty for that part of his effort that had been intuitive—his 'feelings' as he used to call them.

Smeaton had known only that the power of the Atlantic was enormous. His successors knew how enormous. One of Robert Stevenson's sons, Thomas, devised a marine dynamometer for measuring the force of the waves. He found that in summer the average pressure was 611 pounds a square foot, in winter 2,086 pounds. In stormy weather, however, it rose to 4,335 pounds, and in one particular gale off the west of Scotland he recorded a figure of 6,083 pounds, or nearly three tons. Smeaton's successors had the advantage of knowing their enemy before they started the battle.

In these years the administrative take-over by Trinity House was also completed. The Napoleonic wars were a dimming memory. The machine was making ruthless progress. Railways, bridges, factories were beginning to transform the look of the country. Trade was booming. The lighting of the seas was as important as the lighting of the cities. Successive Royal Commissions condemned the obsolete system of private ownership of lighthouses. In 1836 Parliament consummated a process that had by this time been going on for years with an Act compulsorily transferring all English and Welsh lighthouses to Trinity House (and Scots and Irish lighthouses to their respective authorities). It is indicative of the expansion of trade (and therefore lighthouse dues) that it cost the Corporation £1,000,000 to buy out the nine private owners still left. For the Longships lighthouse they had to pay £37,000, for the Smalls £170,000, and for the Skerries the scarcely credible sum of £445,000.

At last there would be a national lighthouse system worthy of the sailors to whom the nation's safety, welfare, and expanding power owed so much. It was the consummation of the dedicated professional service which was to weave the name of Trinity House into the maritime history of this country in letters of gold. The Royal Academy of the Sea had come of age.

In the previous year, following more alarming reports of the Eddystone 'shake', Trinity House had felt it advisable to issue a precautionary notice to shipping interests that it might in the near future be necessary to abandon the lighthouse. But two years later, when Victoria became Queen, it was still there, and the year after that the interior was strengthened from top to bottom with iron clamps and ties. In addition, the projecting cornice at the top of the tower was reduced in size. It had been put there in the first place to deflect the waves. Now it was thought to be doing more harm than good by providing the sea with a surface to hit.

A decade later the lighthouse was still there, and in 1859— the year in which Dickens published *A Tale of Two Cities*, and three years after Florence Nightingale returned from the Crimea—it was one hundred years old and still standing. The abscess in the red rock was still alarming and the ocean never left it alone, but the tower could still defy it. Even if in the end it had to die, it was already assured of immortality in the scores of lighthouses throughout the world that were now being built in its image. For the concave profile of Smeaton's Eddystone had become the classic outline most favoured by the world's builders. (An interesting exception is one of America's most famous rock lighthouses, Minot's Ledge, which marks the dangerous Cohasset Rocks in the approaches to Boston. An earlier lighthouse having been destroyed in a gale, a new tower was designed by General Barnard, who took as his model, not Smeaton's but Rudyerd's Eddystone, believing that the conical shape, if built of stone instead of wood, would be stronger. This handsome tower, which took five years to build, was completed in 1860 and is the subject of Longfellow's song to a lighthouse. No poet can ever resist a lighthouse.)

The inspiration it had given to others was not, however, the Eddystone's only guarantee of immortality. In 1860 its fame earned it a unique honour: its image appeared on the coinage. The new bronze penny issued in that year showed Britannia flanked by a ship and a lighthouse. Most coinage authorities accept that the Eddystone was the tower represented, a reasonable assumption as its first centenary was being widely acclaimed at the time the artist was working on his design.

The lighthouse remained on the penny until the issue of 1895 from which a new designer removed both ship and lighthouse. Possibly he was a good patriot who felt that Britannia's ruling of the waves was by that time sufficiently self-evident to need no symbolic corroboration. But as he used the extra space to give the lady a slightly fuller skirt he may simply have been a fashion purist.

The lighthouse (but not the ship) reappeared in the design of 1937 and it has adorned the penny ever since.

As more and more modern towers challenged the ocean, the folklore of tempest grew. Time, so far from discrediting the fearful tales of the Eddystone lightkeepers which Robert Stevenson had been inclined to discount, confirmed them. The power of the waves, long since measured in pounds per square foot, was manifesting itself in more picturesque ways.

At the Bishop Rock the sea wrenched a bell from the heavy bracket by which it was fixed to the iron balcony of the lighthouse a hundred feet above. At the Unst Lighthouse—built on a high mound of rock in Shetland—a wall five feet high, two feet thick, was thrown down and a door smashed open 195 feet above the surface of the sea.

The famous Fastnet, built on a ninety-foot pile of rock off the southern tip of Ireland, had more than one story to tell. A three-ton mass of stone was once washed off the top of the cliff, eighty feet above sea-level. Despite the height above the sea of the base of this tower, the power with which the waves could strike it was once demonstrated by the wrenching of a 6-cwt. cask of rain-water from the ropes securing it to the balcony rail 150 feet above the sea. Here, too, waves striking the rock can send up a wall of water sufficient to blot out the daylight from upper rooms of the lighthouse.

The Bound Skerry in Shetland is also built on a high rock, and on one side there is a wall of massive stone blocks. In one storm one of these, weighing over 13 tons, was torn from its resting place 74 feet above sea-level. At Wick breakwater the sea displaced a single mass of concrete weighing 1,350 tons and on another occasion surpassed this effort by shifting a mass weighing 2,600 tons. Both times these concrete masses were moved without their foundations being disturbed.

These were the forces which Smeaton's Eddystone had endured for well over a century: but it was still there. It seemed an age since the engineer had taken six days to journey from London to Plymouth to make his first survey of the Eddystone reef. Trains that travelled at sixty miles an hour had reduced the time to six hours. The first steamship had long since crossed the Altantic to New York. The Americans had had their Civil War. The English Parliament was now the scene of the rivalry between Gladstone and Disraeli. The British Empire was soaring to that peak of prosperity and power for which so much of the world has still not forgiven it.

This lighthouse of a distant age was not only still there, but in 1865 Trinity House had thought it worth while submitting it to yet another major strengthening operation. Very much of an antique now, but still useful. And still there . . .

In 1877 the British Association held its annual assembly in Plymouth. One of the speakers was James N. Douglass, Engineer-in-Chief of Trinity House. Douglass took the opportunity to make public a decision recently arrived at by the Corporation. A survey of the Eddystone had been made by the Deputy Master, a group of Elder Brethren, and Douglass himself. It satisfied them that the undermining of the rock was worse. It was beyond doubt that the sea had enlarged the dangerous abscess. In addition, much of the cement had decayed and the sea had penetrated too many of the joints. They proposed to replace Smeaton's tower with a new one. Douglass was already at work on the design.

The news caused an outcry. To many it was unthinkable on sentimental grounds that this national monument should go. When it was clear that sentiment would achieve nothing, those who were opposed to the idea of a new lighthouse rationalized their prejudice. The matter came up in Parliament. If something had to be done, would it not be better to blow up the reef and remove the need for a lighthouse? Trinity House pointed out that to remove the reef would mean blowing up some two million tons of rock: the cost of doing this would be at least seven times that of building a new tower. Apart from this the Eddystone lighthouse was a vital link in the co-ordinated chain of lights marking the full length of the Channel. This was now its main function—to be a signpost. The fact had to be faced that quite apart from the condition of the rock the present structure was obsolete, inadequate, a charming anachronism.

Smeaton's tower was old and tired, and now it had to go.

CHAPTER TWENTY

A Dream Fulfilled

THE fourth and greatest of the Eddystone lighthouses was
built with a magisterial flourish by James Douglass in
less than four years between 1878 and 1882. Twice as
tall, four and a half times as large as its predecessor, and infinitely more elegant, it was a final monument to the pioneers
who had gone before: a majestic salute by a new world to the
past. For Douglass himself it was the crowning achievement of a
life that had been steeped from infancy in the lore and mystery
of lighthouses.

His father, Nicholas Douglass, had been one of the leading
lighthouse engineers of his day, and young James and his
brother William had spent a romantically roving childhood
accompanying him to the wild inaccessible places to which his
work took him. They picked up their education from such
schools and tutors as happened to be nearest to whatever remote
coastal area their father was attending at the time. They grew
up knowing more light stations than cities: their nurseries were
the rock outposts and lonely headlands of England and Wales.

But if his basic education was a little haphazard, James
learned his trade in a hard practical school. After an orthodox
engineering apprenticeship he was, when only twenty-one,
appointed chief assistant to his father when he was engaged to
build a lighthouse on the formidable Bishop Rock, off the Scilly
Isles. Although Nicholas Douglass retained charge of the
work to the end, as time went on he delegated more and more
executive control of the building to James. It was a good
baptism. It was James whom Trinity House engaged, a few
years later, to build another difficult rock tower, the Smalls off
the south-west tip of Wales, and from this assignment he went
straight to a still more difficult one, the Wolf Rock off Land's
End.

Within the service, the Bishop, the Wolf, and the Eddystone are commonly regarded as the roughest and most exposed of the English frontline posts that face the first impact of the Atlantic. To come to the new Eddystone from the other two was to arrive with the highest possible battle honours.

Douglass had made a great name for himself, both as a practical man—'Mr. Douglass was not only an engineer, but he was a blacksmith, a carpenter, and a mason in his own person, as well as a seaman'—and as a courageous and inspiring leader. It was indicative that Trinity House had made him their Engineer-in-Chief when he was only thirty-six. (His brother William was later to hold the same position with the Irish lighthouse authority.)

Now fifty-two, James Douglass—with his beard, side-whiskers, severe penetrating gaze, and great square head—epitomized the eminent Victorian: a somewhat forbidding figure but tireless, it was said, in his concern for the welfare of those who worked for him, including their spiritual welfare. During the building of the rock lighthouses it was often necessary to work on Sundays. When this happened Douglass expected the men to attend the two religious services which he personally conducted near the building site before and after the day's work. He was equally insistent on sharing the worst of any danger or discomfort that arose in this extremely hazardous work. They called him Cap'n Jim and spoke of him with affection.

During the building of the Bishop Rock lighthouse he and his men camped on a barren uninhabited islet two miles from the rock. Sometimes the weather cut them off for days on end and food supplies ran low. Douglass taught them to live on limpets and puffins' eggs, and in the evenings organized concerts to which he contributed solos on the flute. What the workmen thought of his music is not on record, but the puffins and other birds are said to have found it fascinating, and assembled in large numbers when he played to them from some isolated ledge of rock.

The difference between the technical facilities available to Douglass in 1878 and those with which Smeaton had to make do more than a century earlier is obvious enough and need not be laboured. It may, however, be worth mentioning some of the main aids which made it possible for him to tackle a project so much more ambitious than Smeaton's with an assurance that was almost casual.

First, he had a twin-screw steamer, the *Hercules*, which could steam at 10 knots, carry 120 tons of stone, and had been specially built to combine the functions of transport, barrack, and floating workshop. Secondly, he had pneumatic rock-drills. Thirdly, he had mechanical cranes, winches, and pumps. Fourthly, he had the quick-setting Roman and Portland Cement to obviate all the anxieties on that score that had caused the earlier builders so much trouble.

All this gave Douglass's project a difference in kind which renders futile any comparison of it, as an achievement, with Smeaton's. It would be wrong, however, to think that as a result of these facilities the fourth Eddystone was an easy routine feat of building. It was not. Building on the Eddystone could never be easy. And this particular enterprise had imposed upon it from the start a condition which added immeasurably to the difficulty and danger already inherent in it.

Douglass had to find a new part of the reef on which to build. After a most careful survey the only site suitable for the huge tower he had in mind was in the central ridge of the reef, about forty yards from Smeaton's building. Unfortunately this part of the reef was submerged, even at low water. Before starting to build on a rock which they could not even see, this latest generation of Eddystone builders had first to construct a coffer dam of stone and concrete, a difficult enough task in itself. Then, for many months, they would have to return to it for an hour or two of every tide that the weather permitted, pump the coffer dam dry, and work feverishly to cut and carve the temporarily exposed rock into smooth precise recesses and benches and steps into which, eventually, the foundation stones could be cemented and bolted. With or without machinery it was going to take a long time just to begin this lighthouse.

In his general design Douglass followed the now classic outline of Smeaton, but with an important addition. Instead

of the tower tapering all the way up from its foundation it was
to be mounted on a solid cylindrical stone base forty-four feet
in diameter and tall enough to rise from the foundation rock to
a height of two and a half feet above high water.

The purpose of this cylindrical solid was to break the force
of the waves at the level where their power is greatest and
reduce their tendency to race up the sides of the tower in
strength. On the side, this plinth, being eight feet greater in
diameter than the base of the tower proper, would create a
four-foot ledge (lighthouse men call this the set-off) for use as a
landing stage.

The building was to be constructed entirely of pale-grey
granite from the quarries of De Lank in Cornwall and Dal-
beattie in Scotland. Above the cylindrical base the main
tower would be solid for a further twenty-three feet except for
two water tanks sunk into its centre. Above this level there
would be nine rooms, as against Smeaton's four. The centre
of the lantern would be 136 feet above the level of high water,
as against Smeaton's seventy-two.

Work began in July 1878 and, thanks to the steamboat
Hercules, they were able to continue the season until just before
Christmas. By this time they had made forty landings, ex-
cavated fifteen hundred cubic feet of rock and completed a
quarter of the coffer dam.

Douglass, being responsible for the day-to-day running of his
engineering department at Trinity House, as well as the new
lighthouse, was content to leave much of the direction of opera-
tions on the spot to his two main assistants, his son W. T.
Douglass and a man named Edmond. Only three hours at the
most could be spent at one time on the rock, and the men had
to work up to the waist in water, with ropes around them so
that they could be hauled to the boats if they delayed too long
during a rising tide or if a wave took them by surprise and
swept them into deeper water. As a further precaution they
wore life-belts, and a number of iron stanchions were driven
into the rocks to give them something to hold on to. A look-out
man was permanently posted to give warning whenever a large
wave was approaching. It was difficult, dangerous, and ex-

tremely uncomfortable, and James Douglass, who had started his own career by assisting his father, no doubt felt that it would do his son Willie no harm to have a similarly rough introduction to the family calling.

They were able to resume work in February of the following year, but it was not until June that the coffer dam was finished. Now at last they could really see the rock for the first time and cut it into shape.

Each morning (unless it was very rough) the *Hercules* left Plymouth, arriving at the Eddystone just over an hour later. A large hose was carried from the ship to the coffer dam and as soon as the residue of the previous tide had been pumped out of it a second pipe was taken across from the ship. Through this smaller pipe flowed the compressed air that drove the rock-drills which were now plunged into the bared heart of Eddy-stone to cut it into the form required for the foundation stones. Each of these drills could do the work of ten of Smeaton's Cornish tinners. Submarine dentistry was less laborious now. By August the excavations were ready to receive the granite. The foundation stone was formally laid on 19 August by the Duke of Edinburgh (then Master of Trinity House), who was accompanied by his brother the Prince of Wales (the future Edward VII) and a galaxy of Elder Brethren. By the end of December—when this second working season ended—they had completed the first eight courses of the cylindrical base and were within a few feet of the point where their work would be visible even at high water.

It will be remembered that Smeaton's working seasons—at the mercy of sail and oarsmanship—could be sustained only between July and October of each year. Thanks to the *Hercules*, Douglass's men could work at the rock from late February to December. In the last week of February 1880 they were back at the rock, and within a few weeks had raised the base to its final level, two and a half feet above the high water mark.

The *Hercules* was one of two ships specially built for James Douglass in connection with a previous building operation. Its fittings included a railway running along its deck to the stern, and winches and cranes specially designed for the rapid handling of the great blocks of granite, 120 tons of which it could carry at a time.

As the stones, which averaged between two and three tons, were heaved out of the hold, they were transferred to a bogie which rolled them along the rails to the stern of the ship, where they were fixed to a moving chain which ran over pulleys from this point to the rock. There a crane gently lifted them from the chain and swung them into place. By this means ten blocks an hour could be transferred from the belly of the *Hercules* to the cemented permanence of the place they would occupy in the great tower for the rest of time.

With the base at last well above the water line, the work now broke into a triumphant rhythm undreamed of by Smeaton, as stone by stone the pale-grey tower—at times, in the sunlight, touched with pink—reared upwards to its climax: helped on its way by the broken roar of the donkey engines, the rumble and click of wheels on iron rails, the spasmodic engine sputterings of the swinging crane, the creak of pulleys, the groan of chains.

Stone by stone the tower climbed through that year until 9 November. The 1881 season began in February, and progress was faster still because the upper courses were becoming narrower as the tower tapered, and the walls of the upper rooms did not have to be so thick, so that on 1 June that year H.R.H. the Duke of Edinburgh was again invited to contribute briefly and ceremonially to the masonry—this time to lay the topmost and last stone.

It had been built faster in proportion to its size than any previous tower, and James Douglass attributed this to the special appliances with which the invaluable *Hercules* was equipped. In the three years 2,171 blocks of granite weighing 4,668 tons had been set in place. Nothing would ever move these stones. In addition to being held by cement, each block had a ridge protruding along its top and down one end, these ridges fitting—as with a child's bricks—into corresponding recesses in the bottom, and down the opposite end, of the stones above and alongside. Every piece was thus locked into those that surrounded it.

While the last few stones were being lowered into place work had already started on the interior. Foot by foot the hollow caverns were being turned into apartments where men could live and work.

First, immediately above the water tanks that were buried in the solid and could hold a year's supply, the entrance compartment with its gun-metal door weighing a ton. Above it the engine-room, then the fuel store, and above that the winch-room, from which men and stores could be hauled on to the set-off from boats which had brought them as close as they dared to the rocks. Now the kitchen–living-room with its granite range, like a massive tombstone, on which a kettle would permanently simmer, and incorporating a small oven in which meat could be roasted during those few precious days after a relief when fresh meat was available. In this oven, too, the keepers would bake the bread which they had to make for themselves except during those same few days after a relief, when new loaves arrived from Plymouth.

Above the kitchen–living-room the low-light room. From here two Argand lamps would cast a fixed subsidiary beam on Eddystone's sinister satellite, the shoal named Hand Deeps, three and a half miles away. This beam, projected from three-quarters of the way up the tower, would be quite separate from the main beam from the lantern. Above this room was the bedroom, with three lower bunks curling round it, the three together comprising a semicircle, and above them two more for visitors. Now the service room—operational and administrative control point of the lighthouse, linked by a short iron stairway to the lantern room, sixteen feet tall.

Spiral iron stairways had to be conjured into the tower between these floor levels. Windows and their thick metal storm shutters had to be fitted immovably into the openings cut for them in walls which even in the upper levels of the tower were two feet thick. Finally, the *raison d'être* of the whole enterprise, the lighting apparatus.

Throughout the century the French had been pre-eminent in developing and manufacturing the enormous revolving optics in demand throughout the world since Fresnel first revolutionized lighthouse illumination. Only one English firm, Chance Brothers of Birmingham (now Stone-Chance), had ventured into this specialized field, and it was they who designed and supplied the new Eddystone lantern still there in 1959, though the original oil-lamps had long been replaced with better.

Those first lamps, Argand-type with six-wick burners, were two in number and set one above the other at an interval of five feet. Around them revolved a twelve-sided structure of glass comprising twenty-four six-inch lenses and nearly a thousand curving prisms. This apparatus, ten feet tall and weighing more than seven tons, revolved in near silence on broad stainless-steel rollers and was powered by clockwork, the weight being suspended in a shaft running down the centre of the tower. This simple mechanism was ideal for the purpose, because it could not possibly go wrong unless the keepers forgot to wind up the weight—which they had to do once every hour.

Nor was there any reason why, with a minimum of simple care and maintenance, the lamps should ever go out. The only times when they have were during the two world wars. Then, in common with all other coastal lights, the Eddystone was extinguished—lighting up for a few minutes only as required and ordered each day by the Admiralty. During the second of those wars the lighthouse, so inured to assault from the sea, had the new experience of being attacked from the air. Four bombs straddled the tower, two of them bursting close to it. A faint tremor was felt inside, somewhat less violent, the keepers said, than the fearful shudder they experience a few times every winter in the fiercest of the Atlantic gales. . . .

Before long the invention of the incandescent gas mantle and the pressure lamp, burning vaporized oil, would take lighthouse illumination a stage further. But electricity was not for many years to be practicable for the rock lighthouses. It was not infallible, and lighthouse illumination must be. There was no room for the generators that would have been necessary to manufacture the supply of current on the spot: cables bringing it from land would be subject to the danger of damage either on the sea bed or, more particularly, in the rocky vicinity of the reef. Even in 1959 the Eddystone would still be using two paraffin pressure lamps, not much bigger than the household

LOOKING UP FROM SET-OFF

LOOKING DOWN FROM
GALLERY

12-FOOT OPTIC, 1882

,000 candlepower, still in use 1959

NEW 3-FOOT OPTIC

570,000 candlepower, ready for
installation with the electrification of
Eddystone, 1959–60

EDDYSTONE AND THE SMEATON 'STUMP'

THE AUTHOR LEAVING THE LIGHTHOU

Tilley, and the twelve-sided maze of lenses and prisms which the Chance Brothers built in 1882.

By the modern system of evaluating light intensity Smeaton's original twenty-four tallow candles are estimated to have produced something like 67 candle-power. The introduction in 1810 of Argand lamps and catoptric reflectors raised the strength of the lantern to 1,125 candle-power. In 1845 a non-revolving Fresnel dioptric frame—rather like a glass bee-hive made up of prisms and lenses—stepped it up to 3,216 candle-power. In 1872 a better lamp increased the candle-power figure to 7,325. Only ten years later Douglass's first apparatus jumped the figure to 79,250. In 1959 the same optic was producing a beam of 358,000 candle-power. The Eddystone light had come a long way.

It was not until quite recently that new equipment became available which made electrification of the rock lighthouses at last practicable. In particular, compact diesel generators now existed which could be fitted into the cramped accommodation of these towers. In 1959 Trinity House put in hand the electrification of Eddystone. Three small generators, each capable of sustaining the light by itself, were installed in one of the lower store-rooms. As Douglass's tower approached its eightieth birthday the great twelve-foot revolving optic, that had for so long transfigured two small paraffin lamps to 358,000 candle-power, would be replaced by a neat three-foot optic able to convert a 1,250-watt lamp into a beam of 570,000 candle-power. But in 1882 this final apotheosis of the Eddystone light was a long way off. . . .

In the early part of 1882 when the finishing touches were being given to the paintwork and the fittings, Trinity House issued a notice of which this is an extract:

February 24th, 1882.

NOTICE TO MARINERS

English Channel
New Eddystone Lighthouse

Notice is hereby given that, at the latter end of March, the character of this light will be altered, becoming thenceforward a white double-flashing half-minute light, showing two successive flashes of $2\frac{1}{2}$ seconds' duration, divided by an eclipse of about 4 seconds, the second flash being followed by an eclipse of about 21 seconds. The light will be visible all round the horizon, and in clear weather at a distance of $17\frac{1}{2}$ miles.

A white fixed subsidiary light will also be shown from a window in the lighthouse below the flashing light to mark the Hand Deeps.

The new light was actually lit for the first time on 18 May.

Douglass had estimated that the work would take five years; experts said he was being over-optimistic; in fact, it had been finished in three and a half. He estimated that the lighthouse would cost £78,000. A leading engineering journal said that it would be remarkable if the cost was kept down to anything like £80,000. The actual cost in the end was £59,250.

In June James Douglass received a letter from the Prime Minister, Mr. Gladstone, informing him that the Queen proposed to confer on him a knighthood 'on the occasion of the completion of the new Eddystone lighthouse, with which your name is so honourably connected'.

But this was not quite the end of the story. As the superb new lighthouse neared completion, the people of Plymouth became suffused with emotion about the fate of the Smeaton tower, which now looked so small and ancient beside it. They asked if the Trinity House engineers could, before dispersing, dismantle the old lighthouse and transport the stones to Plymouth so that it could be re-erected on the Hoe. They would open a fund to raise locally the money necessary to pay for this. Trinity House agreed, and Sir James Douglass deputed his son Willie to carry out the operation. It nearly ended in tragedy.

The lantern and superstructure having been disposed of, Willie Douglass was standing one day on the now bare summit of the tower, supervising the sheer-legs that was hoisting a crane on to the rocks below. Suddenly the sheers collapsed and one of the heavy legs knocked him over the edge. As he went somersaulting down the seventy feet to the rocks a great Atlantic roller came sweeping in from the west just in time to cover them with a cushion of water and break his fall. He was able to swim into the rocks, suffering from nothing worse than shock and a few bruises. After a week in bed he was back at work.

In due course the tower was taken down as far as the solid. The upper half of it was rebuilt on the Hoe, where it stands today, painted in unattractive seaside promenade colours, a peepshow for tourists. The fate of the undismantled stump was in the end more dignified. It stands as solid as ever on the undermined rock on which John Smeaton built it more than two hundred years ago. Black and brown with time, it draws irresistibly to its barren amputated crown the flocks of sea-birds that cannot tear themselves away from this wild reef which they have haunted for centuries.

So ended something which had started a long time before and had passed through many trials. Centuries ago this violent collusion of rock and ocean had created a legend of super-stitious dread. In time the superstition had given way to a dream. Once, twice, three times the dream had blazed into actuality, but each time the ocean had struck back and eventually it had always won.

Now the struggle was ended. In beauty and arrogance the slender red-crowned Eddystone emerged for the twentieth century from a dream that was now fulfilled.

CHAPTER TWENTY-ONE

Lantern Gallery, Midnight

T HE sea is round. A quivering disc far below and, when there is no moon, tar-black except where three splayed lines of rock gash the waters into whiteness and the spray flies upward like smoke from an explosion. This is the centre of a private world where all is round, so round that after a time it can daze and bemuse the senses into a craving for a single angle or straight line. The beams of light, six pairs of them equidistantly spaced, reach down to the horizon and, sweeping smoothly round it, sever the sea from the ocean beyond. This is the only sea; at night on the Eddystone there is no other.

Behind the screech of the wind and the roar and splash below, the only sound is the hum of the tall lantern, turning ceaselessly and with massive gentleness on rollers of polished steel, making the beams that reach out to the horizon: the serrated panels of its thousand prisms bending and boosting the glow within to inconceivable candle-power. In the lonely midnight this might be the hub of a celestial carousel with mermaids and dolphins riding the tips of the beams where they dip out of sight behind the horizon.

On the open gallery outside the glass wall of the lantern room a man crouches, tensing himself against the wind that seeks to tear him from his handhold on the red railing. He forces his way round the narrow iron walk to the one place where he can escape the wind—the few inches diametrically opposite the point where, on the other side of the round glass wall, it strikes the tower and is cut in two. As the two streams screech past the lantern room to re-unite they leave this small wedge of silent calm, barely as wide as the man's shoulders. In this haven he is safe.

The spokes of light, smoothly revolving, sweeping the circumference of the round sea—his sea—are soothing, and as the lantern continues its serene motion behind him, its prisms lattice his face and his blue jersey with a moving pattern of criss-cross rainbows. It is his first night back. In the cold aloneness of this high place the world he left that morning is already a distant memory. This for him is the universe: the rocks, each one of which he knows as an individual, the spokes of light that will turn until daybreak, the round sea that is always the same and always different.

That morning he left Plymouth at ten, joking as usual with the crew of the tugboat about the prospect of a landing being impossible when they arrived. It was calm enough in the Sound, but when the tug had left the breakwater some way behind the sea became rougher, as it usually did. The tug rolled a great deal, and the swift, choppy waves frequently splashed over its bows. There was low cloud and visibility was not good, but his eyes were instinctively drawn to the point on the horizon where soon he would see first a speck, then a faint line as slender as a hair, then, quite positively, what must be a tower with a tiny blob at its side.

He had done this many times before, but his eyes had to strain to pick it up at the earliest possible moment, as though a compass needle in his brain were controlling the direction of his gaze. It became plainer, a tapering tower flanked by the low stump of its predecessor, and soon they were close enough to see the waves breaking over the rocks. It was not going to be easy. An hour and a half after leaving the docks, the tug anchored a quarter of a mile from the reef. The clean grey tower, topped with brilliant red paintwork and at its base a broad white stripe, towered hugely above them as they approached in the small boat to which they had transferred from the tug.

He was now wearing a life-jacket, and it was taking all the strength of four boatmen to bring the boat in close. The two in the stern sat down and pulled normally on their oars: the other two stood and pushed on theirs, for it was necessary for the tugmaster, who was one of them, to control the final approach and what they then had to do. He took them in a wide sweep outside the eastern ledge of the reef and into the channel between it and the central ledge on which the tower stood. The tower now loomed frighteningly above them, and as the channel narrowed the small boat seemed to be surrounded all of a sudden by sharp, hostile rocks. They were in the lion's mouth.

From the stern they dropped an anchor but continued to row towards the tower. As soon as they were close enough a man on the set-off—the one who was due to be relieved and would go back with them—threw two lines that were attached to the base of the building. The boatmen who were forward seized these and pulled on them till the boat had advanced far enough to tauten the anchor line behind them. Now secured fore and aft, the boat was confined, though nothing could control its alarming rise and fall in the cauldron in which it was now tossing.

As soon as this had been done another rope was thrown and one of the men quickly tied in it the small loop which seamen call a bowline. The distant end of this rope was wound round the winch in the winch-room half-way up the tower. The man they had brought from Plymouth carefully placed a foot in the bowline, wrapped his other leg over the top of it to secure his foothold. The men in the winch-room began to haul him upwards, and one of the boatmen controlled the angle of the rope and its tension from the boat, feeling the tension gently and skilfully as he might a horse's mouth. Clinging with numbed hands to the rope, surrendering like a sack to the strength and dexterity of the others, the man was slowly pulled upwards across the heaving waters and the sharp rocks which—though he could not see them because his back was towards them and it was awkward to turn his head—he sensed were snapping at him viciously.

When at last he was over the set-off—which, because it was low water, was many feet above the level from which he had been hoisted—the boatman controlling the tail of the rope slackened it so that the man could alight on the landing place. Now the dog steps. Awkwardly trussed in the thick life-jacket, he climbed these carefully, placing his foot on them sideways and with deliberation, for they were narrow. A fly on a monstrous round wall, he made his way up the steps slowly, looking neither down at the sharp rocks nor up the great tower, which from this angle seemed to reach to the sky.

Long before he had climbed to the entrance door the first of the boxes of stores was on its way up, and by the time he reached the winch-room they were glad of his help, for it was heavy work hoisting these loads, including himself, by hand. When the last of the filled boxes had been lifted into the tower and the last of the empty ones had reached the boat, the man who had been helping from the set-off was lowered by rope into the boat. It had taken a little more than half an hour from the time the boat had been made fast.

Even in the middle of the twentieth century no one enjoyed these reliefs. They were always difficult and everyone was always glad when they were over. On an average only five of the year's twelve reliefs took place on the intended day. The fact that they were so often several days overdue added to the tension: everyone involved was fretful and impatient and on edge. Reliefs were dangerous and tricky. But they were the most important thing that happened to a lighthouse keeper, the only punctuation marks in the unbroken sameness of his detached life.

A relief was more than a matter of a man coming and a man going. It was a momentary touching of hands with another world, the human world. It was letters from home. It was fresh meat and vegetables for a few days, and professionally baked bread. It was the prints of the photographs taken weeks before; the surprise of a parcel of books; gossip about other members of the service; the excitement, for men living in isolation, of listening to a man just back, telling of what he has seen and done in another existence. For men so alone, every relief was a minor Christmas morning as they searched through the provision boxes for things that meant so much to them: the particular brand of this or that, the small comfort forgotten the last time.

For the man who had come back feelings were bound to be mixed—like school. Sorry the holiday is over, but glad in a way to be back. One month in every three was more holiday than most people had, and after two months on the rock you had enough money to make the holiday worth-while. And yet —and yet—it was always a little strange to be back.

That had been this morning. Already it seemed a long time ago. Only when he was alone again doing his first night watch could he really begin to feel that he was back and that he did not mind. On this first night he was more sharply aware of things he normally took for granted. The shrill mastery of the wind-scream over all other sound, especially inside the heart of the tower. The cleanness of everything, a special pride: metal highly polished or vividly painted, whitewashed walls as aseptic as a hospital or ship, black slate floors as glazed as marble. And the birds. The birds were so much a part of the Eddystone that you lived with them as profoundly as you lived with the other two men. The great colonies that clustered each morning on the Smeaton stump as if paying homage to his memory; the jackdaws that paid unexpected visits from France or England; the occasional migrants, unused to this place, that became demented by the flashing light and, flying into the glare of it, smashed their beaks and sometimes a pane of heavy glass and fell dead on the lantern gallery.

A herring gull once incensed a testy keeper by flying off with a piece of bacon left near the open kitchen window. Next day he placed there another piece which he had poisoned with potash. The gull took it, but to his surprise it was back two days later, looking for more. A more charitable man rewarded it with a titbit and watched it fly off. It swooped straight to the sea and with a quick shake of its head washed what was in its beak before swallowing it. Thereafter it became a regular visitor, but never again did it swallow what it was given before first dipping it in the sea, and they grew to love it. There were times when the birds were better company than the other men.

And the fishes. Staring at the sea and trying to read the intentions of the wind, the man in the blue jersey wonders whether it will be possible to fish later in this day that for him has already started with the middle watch. Fishing with a kite is what he best likes to do. No one can say when kite-fishing first started, but this ancient method practised by the lighthouse keepers is generally thought to have begun at Eddystone, as it is older than the oldest can remember, and at Eddystone the sea is seldom placid enough to be fished from the rocks or from the set-off at the base of the tower.

The canvas of the kite must be strong and the framework of metal. The tail is a heavy cord the length of the tower and a dozen hooks are attached to the last few feet of its great extent. As the wind wrenches the kite away from the gallery at the top of the tower, the cord by which it is held is belayed round the railing, for so great is the power of these winds, and so heavy the kite, that if the cord is slipped directly through the hands it will skin them. Skilfully played by the man braced against the rail of the gallery, the kite hovers and plunges a few feet above the deeps beyond the reef, the hooked tail sunk in the water and swept widely through it by the currents. When a fish has been hooked the man pulls with all his strength to raise the floundering kite. Now stabilized by the addition of the fish to the weight of its tail, it is tugged by his strong pull into new flight, and he can draw it into the side of the tower, which it eventually strikes far down, and then it is simply a matter of hauling it up, and the fish with it, to the gallery rail. Often they have caught fish of up to seven pounds by this means. But before he can master this art a man must not only know the ways of the fishes but also the nature and habit of the currents and tides, and their seasonal vagaries, so that the kite can be directed to the right quarter.

These are the things which, after many years, the lighthouse keeper comes naturally to know: the fishes and the birds, the way of the winds, and the changing moods of the sea. In the end he may understand and know them better than he understands and knows his colleagues, and in the end he can grow to love them best.

The lantern is now alone. The man has gone below to call his relief. The beams continue to sweep the edge of the round black sea, six beams in pairs and spaced to give their message to any who may see them, two searing flashes in each half minute. Far below, the ocean and the red rocks continue their endless striving for a mastery that neither will ever achieve. The south-west wind from the Americas shrieks past the tower, making unearthly music as it is torn by the tiny flute-holes of the windows.

Bibliographical Note

Documentation and serious literature relating to English lighthouses is extremely limited, the more so because on three occasions in its long history Trinity House has lost most of its records through fire, the last being in 1940 during the bombing of London. For the main factual content of this history I have relied almost exclusively on such contemporary or nearly contemporary sources as exist, of which the chief are the following:

SAMUEL PEPYS. *Diary* and *Naval Minutes*. 1660–83.
JOHN EVELYN. *Diary*. 1641–97.
N. LUTTRELL. *A Brief Relation*. 1697.
H. WINSTANLEY. *Edystone Lighthouse, Narrative of the Building*. 1699.
Calendar of Treasury Papers. 1702–7.
DANIEL DEFOE. *The Storm*. 1704.
The Spectator. 1712.
B. F. DE BELIDOR. *Architecture Hydraulique*. 1743.
Philosophical Transactions of the Royal Society. 1755.
WALPOLE. *Catalogue of Engravers*. 1786.
JOHN SMEATON. *Narrative of the Building and a Description of the Construction of the Edystone Lighthouse with stone*. Second Edition (corrected). 1793.
Letters and Important Documents relative to the Edystone Lighthouse selected by Robert Harcourt Weston from the correspondence of the late Robert Weston. 1811.
BRAYBROOKE. *History of Audley End*. 1836.
A. STEVENSON. *Lighthouses, A Rudimentary Treatise*. 1850.
S. SMILES. *Lives of the Engineers*. 1862.
D. STEVENSON. *Lighthouses*. 1864.
T. STEVENSON. *Lighthouse Illumination and Construction*. 1881.
PRICE EDWARDS. *Eddystone Lighthouses*. 1882.
Plymouth Institution, *Transactions*. 1887–90.
T. WILLIAMS. *Life of Sir James Nicholas Douglass*. 1900.
H. F. WHITFELD. *Plymouth and Devonport*. 1900.
The Geological Memoirs.

The following modern works were consulted:

British Lighthouses. J. P. BOWEN (Longmans, Green, 1946).
Trinity House. COMMANDER HILARY P. MEAD (Sampson Low, 1947).

The Story of Plymouth. R. A. J. WALLING (Westaway Books, 1950).

The Navy of Britain. MICHAEL LEWIS (Allen and Unwin, 1948).

Le Phare de Cordouan. J.-FERNAND LANOIRE (1953, Imprimeries Delmas).

English Lighthouse Tours. Ed. by D. Alan Stevenson from the Diaries of Robert Stevenson (Nelson, 1946).

The Pharos of Alexandria. Summary of an essay by Don Miguel de Asin communicated by the Duke of Alba to the British Academy (Humphrey Milford, 1933).

The Essex Review. (1918–20).

Index

Albrow, the, 86
Alexander, Field-Marshal Viscount, 13
Alexandria, Pharos at, 6–7
al-Shaikh, Ibn, 6
Anne, Queen, 56; death, 89
Argand, Aimé, 178; his lamp, 178–9, 198, 199
Asin, Miguel de, 6
Attlee, Earl, 13
Audley End, 28–9; Winstanley's engravings of, 35

Bacon, Sir Francis, 17
Baldwin, 1st Earl, 13
Barnard, General, 187
Beacon-towers, early, 5, 7–8
Belidor, 10
Biscay, Bay of, 7
Bishop Rock lighthouse, 188, 191, 192
Bound, James, 56
Bound Skerry lighthouse, 189
Box, Mr., quarry owner, 134
Bridge, Captain Timothy, 45
Brittany, wreckers in, 21

Caister lighthouse, 11
Camden, William, 2
Carter, Henry, 167
Casquets, the, 3
Catherine the Great, Empress of Russia, 174
Cawsand Bay, 100, 134, 147
Cement, 153–4
Chance Brothers, 198–9
Charles II, King, 29, 33; and restoration of Trinity House Charter, 18; and Mathematical Wing at Christ's Hospital, 19

Charles Gally, the, 86
Charming Sally, the, 162
Cheetham, Alderman, 89
Christ's Hospital, establishment of Mathematical Wing at, 19
Churchill, Sir Winston, 17
Clive, Robert, 111
Cordouan islet, 7–8; Tour de, 9–10
Cornwall, wreckers in, 21
Cromwell, Oliver, and dissolution of Trinity House Charter, 18

Dashkoff, Princess, 174
Defoe, Daniel, 58
Dodman Point, 151
Douglass, Sir James, 189; early life and work, 191–2; awarded knighthood, 200
Douglass, Nicholas, 191
Douglass, William, 191, 192
Douglass, W. T., 194, 200–1
Dover, the Pharos at, 5
Dungeness lighthouse, 11

Eddystone Boat, 124, 132, 155
Eddystone rocks: position and configuration, 1; roughness of sea around, 1–2; early references to, 2; difficulties of building on, 26, 37 ff.; *First lighthouse*: Winstanley's attempt begins, 40 ff.; second season, 44–7; third season, 47–50; light first lit, 49; plan for strengthening and enlarging, 51; destruction of in great storm, 64; *Second lighthouse*: beginning of, 73; use of wood for, 76–7; design of, 77; work on base, 79–83; timber casing for tower, 84–6; success of

211